From 2017 application

C000043963

DEDICATION

THIS BOOK IS DEDICATED TO EVERY ASPIRING MEDICAL STUDENT. MEDIC MENTOR IS HERE FOR YOU FROM YOUR FIRST STEP, THROUGHOUT MEDICAL SCHOOL AND ON THE JOURNEY TO AN EXCITING CAREER AS A MEDICAL PROFESSIONAL.

MEDIC MENTOR - MOTIVATING MEDICAL MINDS.

YOUR HEALTHCARE CAREER STARTS HERE...

NATIONAL HEALTHCARE WEEKEND

" It just blew my mind! I met healthcare professionals who were honest and now I feel as though I have made an informed decision to pursue the career that I really want. I have been to similar events before but there is just nothing this good! "
Sophie Bridgewater Year 12

ALL PHOTOS ARE FROM REAL MEDIC MENTOR EVENTS

THREE TIMES EACH YEAR IN:

NOVEMBER, MARCH & JULY

- LONDON
- BIRMINGHAM
- LANCASTER
- CARDIFF
- NOTTINGHAM
- STIRLING

Medic Mentor
Motivating Medical Minds

CHOOSE FROM 7 HEALTHCARE CAREERS

National Weekend is made up of conferences and UCAS lectures, each dedicated to 7 specific healthcare careers:

- Medicine
- Dentistry
- Veterinary Medicine
- Nursing
- Midwifery
- Psychology
- Biomedicine
- Pharmacy

FIND OUT WHY OVER 6000 PEOPLE HAVE JOINED MEDIC MENTOR

AT MEDICMENTOR.CO.UK

UK'S LARGEST HEALTHCARE CAREERS EVENT

With over 30 conferences at 5 locations across the UK on the same weekend! Over 800 healthcare professionals teaching 2000 aspiring students from 800 schools!

Suitable for students in year 10-12. Parents and teachers are also welcome.

Proceeds from these events are reinvested to support the next generation of our UK's Healthcare professionals with scholarships and free educational initiatives.

Medic Mentor is a National Medical Organisation dedicated to mentoring aspiring healthcare students.

Medic Mentor
Motivating Medical Minds
medicmentor.co.uk

The UK's largest Academic Network for Aspiring Medics

Free Weekly Medical Webinars

YOUR HEALTHCARE CAREER STARTS HERE...

Free Access to a Doctor or Medical Student for 1 hour every week!

Webinar Topics:

Personal Statements | Medical School Societies | Work Experience | Ethics | UKCAT | BMAT | Applying for Scholarships | Volunteering | Research and Publishing | PBL | Selecting your Medical Schools | Current Affairs | Gap Years | Clearing

Why Choose Us?

* Medic Mentor is a Social Enterprise that reinvests proceeds from events, books and the Summer School back into scholarships and free educational resources. We also provide free places for students from low-income backgrounds.

* We don't just help you to get into Medical School - we also support you throughout your medical degree too!

* Join our thriving community by registering for a free online account and get involved in organsing and participating in our nationwide events!

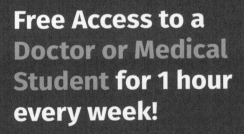

Over **2000 Mentors** teaching nearly **6000 Applying Students** from over **800 Schools** across the UK

Click on the webinar link
A new link will be emailed to you so that you can access the Webinar talk, at a specific time each week. Create a free Medic Mentor account to stay in the loop!

Live chat allows you to ask questions
An interactive live chat function will give you a chance to post your queries to the Mentor presenting the talk.

Download the free handout
You will then be able to download the handouts from your free Medic Mentor student account at medicmentor.co.uk!

Mastering Medical School Conference

Held Annually at the
University of Nottingham

Medical **Protection**

The Royal College of Pathologists
Pathology: the science behind the cure

RC PSYCH
ROYAL COLLEGE OF PSYCHIATRISTS

MDU

WORK THE WORLD
Healthcare Electives Overseas

ANTHONY NOLAN
saving the lives of people with blood cancer

WESLEYAN
we are all about you

Speakers Include the Founders of...

The Unofficial Guide to Medicine

Medic Footprints

GEEKY MEDICS

synap

Medic Mentor
Motivating Medical Minds

MEDICAL PROJECTS

44 New Education Scholarships
Priority Access and Exclusively for Medic Mentor Students!

Register your place at www.medicmentor.co.uk

Summer School
Medicine | Dentistry | Vet Med

Medic Mentor
Motivating Medical Minds

UK Medical/Dental/Vet School Applications

Mentor Helpline: 07454 704 204 - **Email:** admin@medicmentor.org - **Website:** www.medicmentor.co.uk

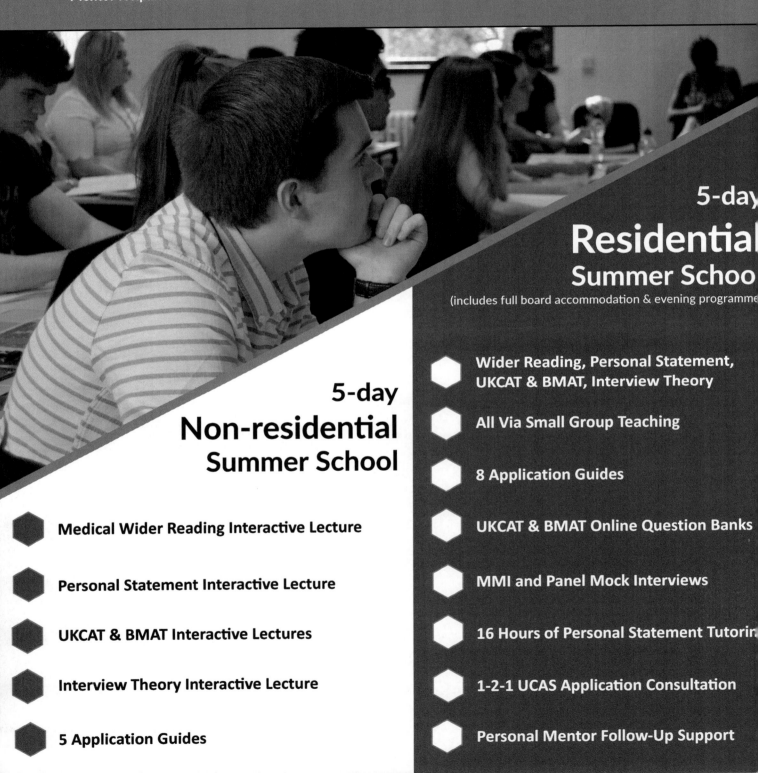

5-day
Residential
Summer School
(includes full board accommodation & evening programme)

- Wider Reading, Personal Statement, UKCAT & BMAT, Interview Theory
- All Via Small Group Teaching
- 8 Application Guides
- UKCAT & BMAT Online Question Banks
- MMI and Panel Mock Interviews
- 16 Hours of Personal Statement Tutoring
- 1-2-1 UCAS Application Consultation
- Personal Mentor Follow-Up Support

5-day
Non-residential
Summer School

- Medical Wider Reading Interactive Lecture
- Personal Statement Interactive Lecture
- UKCAT & BMAT Interactive Lectures
- Interview Theory Interactive Lecture
- 5 Application Guides

For available dates and to secure your place visit
www.medicmentor.co.uk

Over 90 Scholarships Available Each Year!

For students in any year studying Medicine, Dentistry, Vet Med or Psychology

Apply at
medicmentor.co.uk

Presenter Scholarships

Priyanga Kumar, final year med Student from Leicester, presenting at the Insight into Medicine Conference at UCL

Education Scholarships

George Huntington, final year med student from Sheffield, is the current Publishing Scholar and Editor of the Mentor Magazine

Mentoring Scholarships

Jordan Fisher, 3rd year vet student from the RVC, is a Mentoring Scholar and taught students at this year's Summer School

Medic Mentor

Published by Medic Mentor Publishing Group

Authors:

Caitlin Gibb, Claire Gillon, Lauren Quinn (alphabetical order)

Editors:

Rebecca Yates, Iain Kennedy, Jenardan Sellathurai, Akash Bhalla

ISBN: 978-0-9569720-3-3

Medic Mentor is a registered trademark. Website: www.medicmentor.co.uk. Printed by Medic Mentor Ltd, Essex.

Purchasing any of the Medic Mentor Medical Application Guides does not guarantee a place at medical school and it is the individual student's responsibility to submit an application via UCAS. All advice and information provided by Medic Mentor Ltd is believed to be true and accurate at the date of publication. The company cannot accept any legal responsibility or liability for any errors or omissions made. Medic Mentor Ltd makes every reasonable effort to ensure content accuracy in all of its resources. Due to the dynamic nature of medical school applications however, institutions are constantly updating their course details. To read the full disclaimer visit www.medicmentor. co.uk/disclaimer.

All of the information contained within this guide falls under the copyright of Medic Mentor Ltd. The content of this book cannot be reproduced in any form, without the express permission of Medic Mentor Ltd or one of its appointed representatives. Therefore, please do not photocopy any of the pages in this book

© Medic Mentor Ltd

CONTENTS

Medical Schools Compendium

PART 2: MEDICAL SCHOOLS

4

DR REBECCA YATES, DIRECTOR OF EDUCATION

FOREWORD

Deciding to apply to university can be a daunting task. The challenges of learning to fend for yourself (no, you can't cook pasta by putting it in the kettle) as well as succeeding academically, often prove to be a delicate balancing act. That said, university also provides you with the opportunity to explore new things in a supportive environment (sports, foods and even quidditch.)

Choosing the university that is right for you has never been more important. With medical students ranked against their cohort nationally for jobs after graduation, succeeding academically can be crucial. Whilst league tables with various scoring criteria exist, learning and living environments vary greatly between institutions and an environment that suits one student may be detrimental to another. Small group teaching requiring regular student contributions may strike fear into one student but allow another to thrive as they share knowledge. As you read through the Medical Schools Compendium (MSC) you should spend some time reflecting our your own 'marking criteria', keeping track of pros and cons.

Making these choices is an incredibly exciting time; narrowing down your four choices from the thirty-six available can be quite an adventure. Don't forget to involve those closest to you and enjoy exploring your favourite university, city and campus. I remain forever grateful to my Dad who drove me around the country to open days, loaded the car with all my worldly possessions and carried them up multiple flights of stairs at their destination without compliant. Enjoy your journey, keep the MSC close at hand and don't forget to stay in touch with the team at Medic Mentor.

The Medical Schools Compendium Author Team

THE MEDICAL SCHOOLS COMPENDIUM WAS RESEARCHED AND WRITTEN AS PART OF MEDIC MENTOR'S EDUCATION SCHOLARSHIP PROGRAMME. THE TWO MEDICAL STUDENT AUTHOR'S SPENT A YEAR RESEARCHING AND WRITING THE COMPENDIUM UNDER THE GUIDANCE OF THEIR JUNIOR DOCTOR MENTOR (MEDI), DR. CLAIRE GILLON, WHO IS A STRONG ADVOCATE OF PEER-LEARNING, ACADEMIC STUDY SKILLS AND PROGRESSIVE MEDICAL EDUCATION INITIATIVES.

CAITLIN GIBB

AUTHOR & SCHOLARSHIP HOLDER

Caitlin is now in her fourth year at Barts and the London Medical School. She remains open-minded about a future specialty but has a developing interest in psychiatry, for which she has attended multiple taster courses. Last academic year, she was awarded the scholarship role of Summer School Mentor, supporting students in their UCAS applications.

DR. CLAIRE GILLON

AUTHOR & EDUCATION MEDI

Claire is a Foundation Year Two (FY2) doctor with a wide range of additional interests. At Manchester University, she studied the Anatomical Sciences BSc along with Japanese. Progressing into medical school, she contiuned her commitment to languages by completing a 16-week elective in Berlin. She is also a qualified Tai Chi instructor.

LAUREN QUINN

AUTHOR & SCHOLARSHIP HOLDER

Lauren is a final year medical student at the University of Birmingham. She is interested in an academic career in diabetes and endocrinology, and has led the Birmingham Academic Medicine Society (BAMSoc). In addition to organising conferences, Lauren has created multiple teaching training events and remains committed to peer-learning in medicine

How to use the Medical Schools Compendium

The medical schools compendium (MSC) will give you an overview of the medical schools in the UK, their course structure, entry requirements and items for consideration.

We recommend that you read the MSC from start to finish. We certainly advise students to read the 'Definitions' and 'Universal Requirements and Application Basics' pages prior to reading the medical school factsheets within the compendium, as this will aid your understanding and help you to make more sense of all the information provided.

When looking at the admissions data please be aware that the number in brackets correlates to the number of allocated spaces for international students. When detailing entrance exam scores, the year written relates to the year of entry to the medical school e.g. UKCAT 2017 -2770 would mean the UKCAT score for Sep

2017 entry was 2770 - and so often the test will have been taken in 2016 (i.e. the year when UCAS applications are submitted for 2017 entry).

We realise that there is an overwhelming volume of information found herein and so have provided an interactive companion which can be used alongside this book to help you along the way to narrowing down your choice of medical schools. The information is designed to be easily digestible and the worksheets allow you to outline your thoughts throughout the process.

We hope this guide is of great benefit to all students applying for medicine. As medical students who have been through the process ourselves, we know how daunting a task it can be but know that it is so very worth it in the end!

Universal Requirements and Application Basics

As you will see in the following pages there are many unique characteristics amongst the thirty-six institutions. However there are a few areas required as standard by all medical schools.

GRADES	Grades AAA at A level or equivalent are required, unless applying via a "non traditional" route. Chemistry A level or equivalent is always required. Biology may or may not be required but a second science is needed. In science subjects, the majority of universities require a pass in the practical endorsement component, where applicable. The third subject can often be a non-science, but check university preferences. As a general rule, most universities will accept modular resits within the two year window, however retaking post-16 exams outside of the two year window, will only be accepted in cases of extenuating circumstances, to be discussed with the admissions team. GCSE weighting varies but generally, excellent grades are preferable. Applicants often attain very similar academic scores because of the high number of excellent grades. Therefore, admissions tests often form a major selection component for interview, but exact weighting varies between schools.
ADMISSIONS TESTS	There are 3 different tests: UKCAT, BMAT, or GAMSAT. The majority of schools require the UKCAT. Universities use the UKCAT and BMAT scores differently; some will have a minimum cut-off for consideration whereas others will rank all applicants. The admission test may also be used as a decider between applicants following interview. Universities offering both undergraduate and graduate courses may require different tests for each.
PERSONAL STATEMENTS AND ADDITIONAL DOCUMENTATION	Personal statements (and the reference) are now rarely scored or used for interview selection, however they will be screened for core values and red flags. A minority of medical schools also ask applicants to fill in a work experience/volunteering details form including contact information.
INTERVIEWS	The majority of interviews are now Multiple Mini Interviews (MMI). Interview season ranges from November - March and offers may be made on a rolling basis, or after all applicants have been interviewed - the process varies from school to school. Generally, all interviews are aiming to assess your communication skills, commitment and motivation for medicine, and problem solving or scenario interpretation.
RE-APPLICATION AND DEFERRED ENTRY	Most schools allow applicants to reapply, however some set a limit and others will not consider reapplications if the candidate was rejected at interview. Previous applications may or may not be considered. Most medical schools will accept deferred entry to medicine. Some Universities will require the reasoning to be included in the personal statement.

ACCOMMODATION	Almost all medical schools now guarantee accommodation in halls of residence or equivalent for the first year of study.
CURRICULUM	Medical school curriculums vary in terms of style, structure, modules etc. and often change subtly year on year. However, all are GMC regulated and required to meet core standards, hence all medical schools train you to graduate with the same qualification. Following graduation, as you move along your career, the medical school you attended becomes increasingly less significant. Anatomy can be taught via dissection, prosection or virtual learning. There are pros and cons to each method. Medical schools now all incorporate patient contact from the first year of training, and so this is no longer a true differentiating factor between medical schools.
OTHER POINTS	Personal statements (and the reference) are now rarely scored or used for interview selection, however they will be screened for core values and red flags. A minority of medical schools also ask applicants to fill in a work experience/volunteering details form including contact information. All medical schools have their pros and cons and we have presented a few points to consider in the Medical Schools Compendium but wherever possible it is essential to attend an open day, which often gives the chance to speak to students in person.

If you have any further questions, which have not been answered in this guide, make sure you contact the admissions team of the school by telephone or email.

The Application Process

APPLYING TO MEDICAL SCHOOL UNSURPRISINGLY REQUIRES QUITE A LOT OF PREPARATION. WITH MULTIPLE HOOPS TO JUMP THROUGH KEEP IN MIND THE VARIOUS DEADLINES AND STAY ORGANISED.

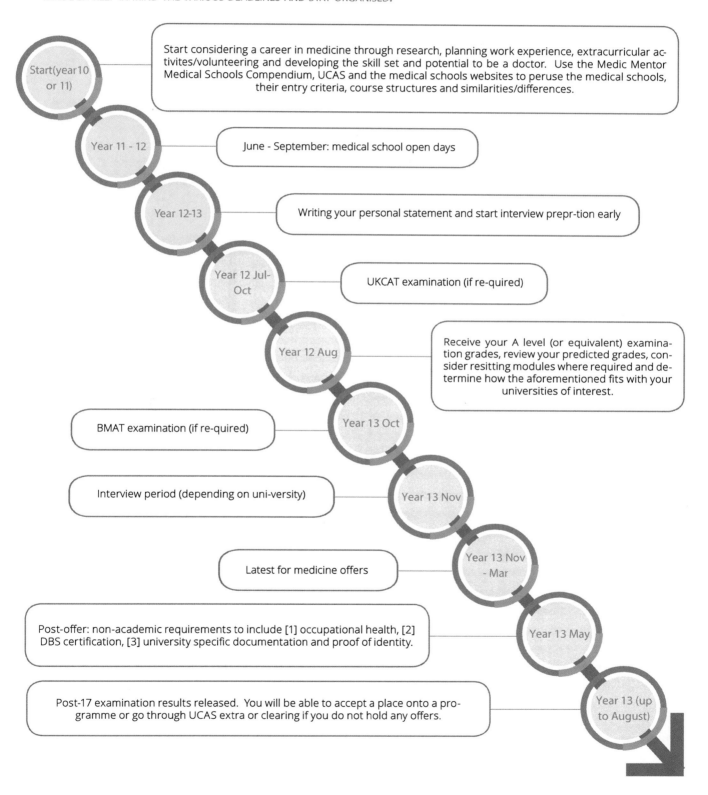

Start (year 10 or 11) — Start considering a career in medicine through research, planning work experience, extracurricular activites/volunteering and developing the skill set and potential to be a doctor. Use the Medic Mentor Medical Schools Compendium, UCAS and the medical schools websites to peruse the medical schools, their entry criteria, course structures and similarities/differences.

Year 11 - 12 — June - September: medical school open days

Year 12-13 — Writing your personal statement and start interview prepr-tion early

Year 12 Jul-Oct — UKCAT examination (if re-quired)

Year 12 Aug — Receive your A level (or equivalent) examination grades, review your predicted grades, consider resitting modules where required and determine how the aforementioned fits with your universities of interest.

Year 13 Oct — BMAT examination (if re-quired)

Year 13 Nov — Interview period (depending on uni-versity)

Year 13 Nov - Mar — Latest for medicine offers

Year 13 May — Post-offer: non-academic requirements to include [1] occupational health, [2] DBS certification, [3] university specific documentation and proof of identity.

Year 13 (up to August) — Post-17 examination results released. You will be able to accept a place onto a programme or go through UCAS extra or clearing if you do not hold any offers.

Defining Terms

THE PURPOSE OF THIS SECTION IS TO DEBUNK THE TERMS YOU WILL COME ACROSS ON UNIVERSITY WEBSITES, ON OPEN DAYS OR SEE MENTIONED IN THIS BOOK.

MEDICINE DEGREE

The title of the degree qualification can vary from university although they all mean the same thing: you have graduated with a degree in medicine. You may see the degree titles have the names MBBS, MBChB or MBBCh.

MASTER'S DEGREE

This is awarded after completing one (or sometimes two) further years of study after a traditional bachelor's degree and often in science will involve a significant element of research. Taught Masters are also available. Some medical degrees offer the option of intercalating in a Masters (and even sometimes a PhD). As with bachelor's degrees this will gain further FPAS points.

A100

This UCAS course code is for the undergraduate medicine course. This is usually five years, with an optional year to intercalate (there are variations to this). The usual framework is two pre-clinical years and three clinical years.

GENERAL MEDICAL COUNCIL (GMC)

They are an independent organisation that determines who is qualified to work as a doctor in the UK. The GMC sets standards for medical students and doctors to maintain a certain level of medical education and practise across the UK.

EXTENDED PROJECT QUALIFICATION (EPQ)

This is an additional qualification that can be completed in your sixth form years. It may not be offered at all schools and so universities do not include it as a requirement. It involves choosing a topic and either completing a research based written report, a production such as a sports event or an original object such as a piece of artwork. Alongside the finished product will be a production log and a presentation given at the end. Universities often welcome it as it shows students can work independently on a project using a lot of skills that is thought to help prepare them for university. It can be used to earn UCAS points and depending on the university may be used, for example, to substitute an AS level.

BACHELOR OF SCIENCE DEGREE (BSC)

This is awarded after completing a three-year science undergraduate degree. In medicine, you can be awarded an intercalated Bachelor of Science degree by interrupting your medical studies for one year and studying another subject in depth.

UCAS COURSE CODES

These are the codes you can use to easily find courses on the UCAS website, although you can also search for the subject. They are also needed on your UCAS application to confirm which courses you have selected to apply for. Listed below are the two main UCAS codes for medicine, but there may be other UCAS codes such as the codes used for the Foundation year programmes, these vary a lot more.

A101

This UCAS code is for the graduate medicine course. This is usually four years, as it is an accelerated course. The framework tends to vary a lot more between universities: often it is in the form of one pre-clinical year and three clinical years or one and a half pre-clinical years and two and a half clinical years.

OCCUPATIONAL HEALTH

All of the universities that offer medicine will have an occupational health department. It basically relates to health in the workplace, it is both to assess and determine if you will be safe and healthy in the workplace and to protect and prevent harm to patients. It is a preventative discipline.

FOUNDATION PROGRAMME AND ACADEMIC FOUNDATION PROGRAMME (FPAS)

This is the programme you apply for in your last year of medical school in order to be able to complete two years as a junior doctor before deciding on speciality training. There is an application form that you will need to fill out and you will need to sit the Situational Judgement Test (SJT). You can get extra points for your application by completing an intercalated BSc, Masters or PhD.

DEFERRED ENTRY

This is where you hold an offer for a place at medical school but take a gap year (normally between finishing A levels and starting the degree). Medical schools normally expect you to declare it on your UCAS application when you apply so they know you will be starting with the following cohort.

PROBLEM BASED LEARNING (PBL)

A small group of students meet together with a supervisor and they work through a case study and come up with some objectives with one of the students allocated the role of chair and one student allocated the role of scribe. Then everybody goes away and researches the chosen objectives. At the next session, each objective is gone through with a discussion of the research findings. There are slight variants in terms of problem based learning, but they do follow the main outline explained.

STUDENT SELECTED COMPONENTS (SSCS)

They form a minimum of 10% of the medical curriculum and offer medical students an element of choice during their degree. The aims include to improve research skills, self-directed learning, a move beyond the core curriculum, self-confidence, presentations, writing, an exploration of career paths and to assist with the choice of intercalated degrees. SSCs vary between medical schools with the type they offer, what year they start offering them (can be from first year or later on) and the amount of time they take up in the curriculum. Look carefully at the medical school websites for more detail on the SSCs they offer.

INTERCALATION

This is a year break in your medicine degree, which involves studying another academic subject for a year: at the end you get awarded a bachelor's science degree (BSc). It may be written as iBSc, indicating that it is intercalated. In some cases you join students who are in their last year of their degree, in other cases the degree might have just been created for medical student intercalation. There may be the option of studying for a Masters instead of a bachelor's degree. The qualification can be used to gain additional points on FPAS, but be aware not all courses are weighted equally for this purpose. There are many options to choose from, a few examples include genetics, anatomy, neuroscience and medical education but there are so many more than that! Intercalation varies between universities as to the subjects offered, whether it is compulsory, what year you are allowed to do it in, and whether you can complete it at another university.

PRIVATE (OR INDEPENDENT) UNIVERSITIES

They are not state-funded and their running costs are funded solely by tuition fees. As their money comes from students, they tend to be very teaching oriented and tend to be less research focused. They are not subject to the same fee cap as state funded universities. There are now three private universities offering medicine.

ELECTIVE

This is part of the medical school curriculum, which enables students to do a placement wherever in the world they want, in whatever speciality they want. It is up to the medical student to organise it and it often runs in 4th or 5th year, lasting from 5-10 weeks depending on the medical school you go to.

SPIRAL CURRICULUM

You learn and re-cap the same topics as you go through medical school; building on complexity and depth as you go back over the topic. A lot of medical schools now incorporate this style of learning.

VALUES BASED RECRUITMENT (VBD)

These are values and behaviours that line up with the NHS values in the constitution. These values may be used/looked at by universities for selection of medical students.

OBJECTIVE STRUCTURED CLINICAL EXAMINATIONS (OSCES)

These are practical examinations that form part of your end of year exams (depending on the university, you might not have to do them in pre-clinical years). They involve going around timed stations, being given a scenario and the student being marked on how well they perform. It varies from communication stations (e.g. breaking bad news, taking a history) to performing basic life support, taking blood from a simulated arm and performing a cardiac examination.

ANATOMY

In medicine this is the study of the structure that makes up humans. Not every university offers dissection and prosection and they may teach anatomy in a different way. Within this book there is a section for each medical school describing the anatomy teaching, it is useful to think about the way you would learn best.

PROSECTION

This is where dissection has already taken place often by a trained anatomist to show specific parts of anatomical interest. It is used for teaching purposes and is usually a body part separately rather than the whole body.

DISSECTION

Full body dissection involves working on a cadaver (a human body that has been donated to medical education) in small groups to remove tissue to identify structures in the human body.

ENTRANCE EXAMS

The three exams used for medical schools in the United Kingdom are UKCAT, BMAT and GAMSAT. The entrance exams are often used to help determine which applicants should be invited to interview as it allows all students to be compared from the same test. It is important to note that universities that offer undergraduate and graduate medicine may ask for different entrance exams for each course. There are costs associated to take the exams but bursaries exist for those in financial need.

MINI MULTIPLE INTERVIEWS (MMIS)

This is a type of interview structure where there are multiple stations, which applicants move around. The stations vary in terms of what you will have to do and depending on the medical school. It could include analysing data, discussing scenarios, doing a role-play or answering questions. Each station tends to last 5-10 minutes. At the end all the scores from the stations are collated to give an interview score. This is becoming an ever-popular method of interviewing medical applicants.

GRADUATE AUSTRALIAN MEDICAL SCHOOL ADMISSIONS TEST (GAMSAT)

This is an entrance exam for graduates and originally used for those applying for the accelerated four-year course. Some medical schools require graduates who are applying for the five-year programme to also take it. The exam includes content that is equivalent to first year degree biology and chemistry and A level physics. There are 3 sections; reasoning in humanities and social sciences, written communication and reasoning in biological and physical sciences. The test lasts 5 ½ hours. The exam takes place on one date in March and one date in September with the results being valid for 2 years. There are specific test centres you have to sit the test in. The cost to take the exam is £255 with an additional £60 fee for a late registration. The website is https://gamsat.acer.org/.

BIOMEDICAL ADMISSIONS TEST BMAT

This entrance exam is used for both undergraduates and graduates. The test involves problem solving, GCSE knowledge of science and maths and essay skills. The test is split into three sections with the first two being multiple-choice: aptitude and skills, scientific knowledge and applications and a writing task. The 2 hour test is done on paper and takes place on one specific day (in 2017 this will be November 2nd) with the results being released in November (in 2017 this will be November 24th). The cost to take the exam is £46 and costs an extra £33 if you submit a late entry. You can normally sit the test at your school or college: your school can register really easily if they are not currently registered. The website is: http://www.admissionstestingservice.org/for-test-takers/bmat/.

UK CLINICAL APTITUDE TEST (UKCAT)

This is by far the most common entrance exam and is used for both undergraduates and graduates. It does not look at science knowledge or work from the curriculum. It focuses instead on the cognitive ability of the applicant. There are 5 sections:

1. Verbal reasoning
2. Quantitative reasoning
3. Decision making
4. Abstract reasoning
5. Situational judgement.

For 2018 entry, decision making will now be used as a sub-test replacing decision analysis used in previous years. Applicants who completed the UKCAT test for 2017 entry got their scores from three of the sub-tests: decision analysis was not used. Therefore, the maximum scores were lower and the thresholds universities used were lower than previous years (these can be seen for each university under their entry requirements). The test is completed on a computer and the results are given to the applicant straight away. The UKCAT can be taken between July and early October and is only valid for the application cycle in the year it was taken. The cost to take the exam ranges from £65 to £85 depending on whether you take it in the summer or after August. The test is taken in UK Pearson VUE test centres, where you can also take your driving theory test. The website is https://www.ukcat.ac.uk/.

A level Resits and Reapplying for Medicine

The transition from GCSE to A Level can be a challenging time and things don't always go to plan. If you find yourself in this situation please seek help from friends, family, teachers (and medic mentor) as soon as possible. Most schools offer the opportunity to resit examinations in order to attempt to improve your grades. This may affect your eligibility to apply to certain medical schools but should not be a barrier to medicine all together if you are suitably informed of your options. Generally, medical schools will accept modular resits for GCSE and A levels within the two years normally taken to complete these courses. A level resits outside of the two years will be accepted in cases of extenuating circumstances. Medical schools usually view re-applications with a clean slate A Land only ask that such applicants can show how they have continued to develop in between application cycles. There are exceptions to this, outlined below.

Reapplication Special Considerations

THE FOLLOWING TABLE INDICATES THE STANCE THAT CERTAIN MEDICAL SCHOOLS TAKE TOWARDS REAPPLICANTS.

CAMBRIDGE	Will be considered if applying to a different college on next attempt.
DUNDEE IMPERIAL LIVERPOOL NORWICH QUEEN'S BELFAST (CAN ONLY APPLY TWICE IF APPLIED TO QUEEN'S PREVIOUSLY) ST. ANDREWS ST GEORGE'S	Can apply a maximum of two times.
ABERDEEN	Can apply a maximum of three times.
BIRMINGHAM KEELE NOTTINGHAM UCL	Reapplication will not be considered if you were rejected at the interview stage.

Resit Rules: Special Considerations

THE FOLLOWING TABLE INDICATES THE STANCE THAT CERTAIN MEDICAL SCHOOLS TAKE TOWARDS RESITS OF EXAMS.

BUCKINGHAM CAMBRIDGE SOUTHAMPTON ST. GEORGE'S UNIVERSITY OF CENTRAL LANCASHIRE	Reject GCSE and A Level modular resits.
CARDIFF LEEDS NEWCASTLE MANCHESTER SHEFFIELD	Can resit but need to provide justifications.
DUNDEE	Reject A Level module resits only.
EDINBURGH NORWICH NOTTINGHAM QUEEN'S BELFAST	Accept only 1-2 A Level module resits.
GLASGOW KING'S	Reject GCSE resitsa only.

University Rankings

University league tables, specifically for medicine, are produced annually by a number of sources including the Guardian, the Independent-Complete University Guide, the Times International ranking and the Telegraph.

Each league table for medicine prioritises different factors but generally marks are given for student satisfaction, graduation prospects, entry tariffs and a value added score by the assessing body, and all of these components are combined to give an overall score and a rank, relative to other medical schools. The different league tables vary quite substantially and no score can be considered superior to another, they simply give a subjective ranking, which may help with your decision-making but the information should not be taken as fact.

Unistats is another popular tool, which provides more detailed breakdown of course information, student satisfaction, employment prospects, cost of living etc, but again the information is subjective rather than objective facts. It is important to remember that unlike most other university courses, Medicine is a very regulated course by the GMC meaning that all medical schools must meet set standards and the medicine final qualification is the same for all medical schools; each medical school will however teach medicine slightly differently with different amounts of time spent in lectures, in small group teaching, in the clinical settings, in anatomy etc. Therefore, the ranking systems tend to identify differences in student satisfaction, which is hard to measure accurately and not always truly reflective of a university.

Therefore, we would advise that you use these ranking systems as a guide, but would not advise you make an informed choice based on these tables alone. All medical schools have their pros and cons and the best way to find these out is to attend the open days and speak to students who attend that university on these days.

Various University Rankings

BELOW ARE THE RANKINGS PRODUCED BY DIFFERENT SOURCES.

Guardian 2017
1. Oxford
2. Cambridge
3. Queen Mary
4. Dundee
5. Exeter
6. Keele
7. UCL
8. Glasgow
9. Swansea
10. Edinburgh
11. Imperial
12. Aberdeen
13. Newcastle
14. Plymouth
15. East Anglia
16. Brighton & Sussex
17. St Andrews
18. Hull York
19. Cardiff
20. Birmingham
21. Leeds
22. Nottingham
23. Bristol
24. Southampton
25. Sheffield
26. Manchester
27. Queen's Belfast
28. Manchester
29. Liverpool
30. St George's
31. King's
32. Warwick

Times 2016
1. Oxford
2. Cambridge
3. Imperial
4. UCL
5. Kings
6. Edinburgh
7. Manchester
8. Glasgow
9. Liverpool
10. Queen Mary
11. Bristol
12. Dundee
13. Leicester

Telegraph 2016
1. Oxford
2. Cambridge
3. Cardiff
4. UCl
5. Imperial
6. Queen Mary
7. Edinburgh
8. Glasgow
9. Newcastle
10. Keele

Independent 2017
1. Oxford
2. Cambridge
3. Swansea
4. Queen Mary
5. Glasgow
6. Edinburgh
7. UCL
8. Imperial
9. Exeter
10. Newcastle
11. Bristol
12. Dundee
13. Keele
14. Cardiff
15. Nottingham
16. East Anglia
17. Hull York
18. Plymouth
19. Leeds
20. St Andrews
21. Birmingham
22. Brighton & Sussex
23. Sheffield
24. Manchester
25. Aberdeen
26. Queen's Belfast
27. King's
28. Leicester
29. Warwick
30. Lancaster
31. Southampton
32. Liverpool
33. St George's

Uni	Overall Score			Satisfaction				Staff/ Student Ratio		Spend per student	Entry	
	Gua	Ind	Tim	Gua-course	Gua-teaching	Ind-overall	Tim-overall	Gu	Tim	Gua	Gua-Entry tariff	Ind-entry standard
Aberd	77	95		97	96	4.17		7		2	222	547
Aston												
Bham	70	95		90	93	4.06		8		3	205	519
BSMS	72	95		98	98	4.46		10		8	183	478
Bristol	64	97	60	83	93	3.92	30	9	15	4	205	539
Buck												
Camb	91	99	91	78	89	3.79	79	6	11	10	241	617
Cardiff	70	95		97	90	4.17		10		9	197	512
Dund	85	96	58	93	95	4.19	38	7	15	5	231	560
Edin	78	97	84	79	85	3.68	74	6	13	9	233	570
Exeter	83	97		96	96	4.22		8		7	241	558
Glasg	80	97	68	92	96	4.07	45	8	16	6	237	572
Hyork	70	96		90	96	3.99		9		3	195	515
Imper	78	97	90	87	90	3.98	84	7	11	8	215	533
Keele	80	96		95	95	4.45		7		4	190	483
King's	42	95	85	62	82	3.44	77	8	11	4	187	469
Lancast		94				4.35						461
Leeds	67	96		95	96	4.05		9		3	209	524
Leics	60	95	55	80	82	3.66	27	7	13	6	198	511
Liverp	57	94	65	75	78	3.62	49	6	12	6	187	479
Manch	61	95	68	79	83	3.85	50	8	13	8	200	509
Newca	76	97		94	96	4.24		7		5	210	543
Norwi	74			96	97			8		3	197	
Notting	64	96		85	91	3.82		7		3	201	531
Oxford	100	100	95	96	99	4.63	85	10	11	10	234	615
Plymou	76	96		96	96	4.23		8		4	197	527
Queen Belfast	60	95		94	97	4.21		11	13	4	198	498
Queen Mary/Barts	89		62	94	95		35	8		7	220	
Sheffi	62	95		94	95	4.24		10		3	192	488
Southa	64	94		85	91	4.03		8		4	189	483
St And	71	95		98	96	4.40		11		3	224	553
St Geor	56	93		82	88	3.87		9		4	189	479
Swanse	80	98		88	93	4.18		6		4		
UCL	80	97	89	88	91	3.86	81	6	10	6	215	557
Warwi	35	95		69	80	3.53		13		2		

Non-academic Requirements

ALONGSIDE ACADEMIC REQUIREMENTS MEDICAL SCHOOLS WILL ALSO SPECIFY OTHER CRITERIA TO BE MET BECOME COMMENCEMENT OF A MEDICAL DEGREE. ALL UNIVERSITIES REQUIRE A SATISFACTORY HEALTH ASSESSMENT AND DBS. SOME INSTITUTIONS WILL ARRANGE THESE ONCE YOUR COURSE HAS STARTED.

VACCINES

Students starting on a medicine degree will need to be up-to date on routine vaccinations and usually need some more such as Hep B. Blood tests may also be needed to determine status of blood-bourne viruses. The university you go to will let you know of the requirements and they can also be found on their website. Normally the university will arrange an appointment in the first term with occupational health to assess your vaccination record, take bloods and offer any additional vaccinations. You do not need to get the vaccinations such as Hepatitis B done before starting the course, unless the university specifically tells you to.

DBS (DISCLOSURE AND BARRING SERVICE)

All universities require students to have a DBS check done prior to starting a medical degree: the student declares any cautions, reprimands or convictions. Each case is assessed individually and declaring something will not necessarily prevent a student from studying medicine. If you have concerns, speak to the university or GMC. The university will arrange for the DBS to be completed, so unless specifically asked you should not arrange this yourself.

FITNESS TO PRACTISE

On entry to medical school, students will undergo an Occupational Health Assessment which includes 'fitness to practise'. These are professional standards that medical students need to adhere to throughout medical school and to be able to graduate with a primary medical qualification. If a medical student's conduct or health is concerning then support and guidance should be given. In some cases, where the conduct or health has impaired their fitness to practise, the student may have to undergo fitness to practise proceedings.

HEALTH

All medical students are required to go to through an occupational health assessment. Universities accommodate students with health conditions and disabilities, and can provide support and adjustments to allow them to complete their medicine degree. Accommodations can also be made at interview if declared before. However, some impairments or health conditions will not allow students to meet the requirements of the GMC at graduation; this may stop you from enrolling or completing the course. Therefore, if you are concerned you can contact the university or GMC directly beforehand to discuss.

GENERAL MEDICAL COUNCIL (GMC) REGISTRATION

After being awarded your medical degree you are automatically entitled to be provisionally registered with the GMC: you are given a primary medical qualification and so can practise medicine under supervision. By its very nature being awarded a medical degree means your university confirms that you are fit to practise under GMC guidance.

ENGLISH REQUIREMENTS

International students who do not speak English as their first language require English qualifications. The International English Language Testing System (IELTS) is the most common listed qualification, although there may be other qualifications accepted depending on the university.

Finance

Financing a degree - any degree - can be a source of anxiety for prospective students (and their parents). The standard option of Student Finance exists to provide support for all. It is important to note that there are specific deadlines for applications to Student Finance. In general, they provide loans to cover tuition fees (up to £9,250 for academic year commencing September 2017) and provide maintenance loans to cover other associated costs such as living expenses. Further information can be found on their website.

It is important to bear in mind that the available finance options for degrees can change depending on economic and political climate. At present there is further support for medical students from NHS Bursaries. Once a student has completed 4 years of medical study they become eligible to apply for these bursaries to cover the cost of tuition fees and a reduced grant for living costs. These are non repayable and may (depending on financial background) be supplemented by student finance loans. This applies to those on foundation courses and those who intercalate - who all receive this additional funding after an initial 4 years of study.

For those on graduate courses, students must self-fund the first £3,465 for the first year of study. Thereafter they are eligible to receive a bursary for £3,465 towards tuition fees each year through the NHS Bursaries Scheme. Student Finance offers loans to cover the remaining difference for years 1-4. Graduates (on either undergraduate or graduate courses) are usually eligible to apply for a Professional and Career Development Loan to the value of between £300 - £10,000.

Finally, many Universities (and some organisations) offer scholarships and bursaries subject to meeting specific (but varied) criteria - information for these can be found directly on their websites. Some Universities will also have money available as a hardship fund for students who find themselves in difficulty during their course.

Please do bear in mind that this information is correct at the time of going to print but is subject to change and so prospective students will need to check with the corresponding websites and companies accordingly.

Languages

For some applicants, the ability to study a foreign language is an important consideration. On the page opposite (p25), is a list of the Universities either offering language tuition or placements abroad as part of a medical degree. Universities not listed below may have the option to take additional classes alongside the medical degree - If this is something that interests you it is best to discuss the possible options directly with each University.

UNIVERSITY	Courses(s)	Languages
ABERDEEN	6 week medical humanities option (during 3rd year) which includes the optional study of languages	French German Gaelic Spanish Swedish
CARDIFF (*)	Erasmus Exchange programme - successful students can study in their chosen country for one module. This is a competitive process and no formal language tuition is offered.	France (4th year) Spain (4th year) Portugal (4th year) Italy (4th year) Germany (5th year)
LIVERPOOL	Can spend a year abroad in China at an English speaking University studying modules in Medicine and Chinese. This extends the degree programme by one year and is usually taken in between 2nd and 3rd year. Entry is competitive and open to students from degrees outside of medicine. Students graduate with "Medicine with a year in China". Graduate entry medicine currently NOT eligible to apply.	Chinese
MANCHESTER (*)	European Studies Option: Apply during the 1st semester of 1st year and undertake language classes from 2nd semester of 1st year until end of 4th year. You will graduate with the degree title "Medicine with European Studies". Additional centres such as the University Goethe centre offer separate language courses.	French German Spanish
UCL	UCL CLIE offer various languages for study as part of an SSC module in years 1 and 2. UCL have a requirement for a grade C in a foreign language at GCSE. They are flexible with this and provide the opportunity for language study as an undergraduate with bursaries available.	Arabic French German Italian Japanese Mandarin Spanish
QUEEN'S (BELFAST) (*)	Opportunity to take a clinical module abroad as part of ERASMUS	

Access to Medicine Courses, Widening Access Courses and Foundation Courses

SOME STUDENTS WISHING TO APPLY TO MEDICINE MAY FIND THAT THEY HAVE NOT PREVIOUSLY STUDIED THE REQUIRED BALANCE OF SUBJECTS OR THAT THEY HAVE NOT MET THE STRICT GRADE REQUIREMENTS FOR THE UNDERGRADUATE COURSE. THERE ARE A SERIES OF ALTERNATIVE OPTIONS, WHICH AIM TO BRIDGE THE GAP AND HELP THESE STUDENTS SUCCESSFULLY GO ON AND STUDY MEDICINE.

ACCESS TO MEDICINE COURSES

Access to Medicine courses are designed to provide an education in biology and chemistry to a similar standard as A levels, such that students become eligible to apply to medicine. They are designed for students who have not studied subjects such as biology and chemistry to A level. The courses are delivered in Further Education colleges and the content covered includes biology, chemistry, maths and physics with the same depth but not breadth as A levels. Students are then able to apply for the A100 programme; universities are quite specific as to which access courses from which colleges they accept and whether they accept access courses at all. So at the same time: it is vital to research the access to medicine courses and ensure the universities you wish to apply to accept these. There is no guarantee having studied an access to medicine course that you will definitely be accepted onto the A100 course.

WIDENING ACCESS COURSES

Widening Access courses are there to encourage applicants to apply from under-represented groups, who have the potential to have a career in medicine. The criteria vary between universities in terms of eligibility (can include living location, household income etc) and academic requirements, so make sure to look carefully at each university. The widening access courses tend to involve studying for an extra year at university before then starting on the A100 course, although there are some which allow you to get lower entry requirements and start directly on the A100 course. It is also worth noting that quite a few universities offer free widening access summer schools for medicine (this is separate to the widening access course); this allows students to get a taster of medicine, studying at university and some help with preparation for applying.

FOUNDATION YEAR COURSES

Foundation Year Courses were set up to provide students an extra year to obtain the necessary scientific knowledge and skills before embarking on a medicine degree. The criteria vary a lot between universities as to who is eligible to apply to their individual programmes. The Foundation Year may be aimed at those who do not have the typical entry requirements i.e. science A levels, IB, Scottish Highers; or alternatively applicants who have been out of education for a while; or applicants who meet certain widening participation criteria. Note - there may be some crossover between whether universities call their programme a foundation year course or widening access course when they both may be based on widening participation criteria. Universities usually allow for transition straight onto their undergraduate medicine degree after successful completion of the foundation year course.

Inter Transfer Courses and Graduate Courses

—

INTER TRANSFER COURSES

This involves starting an appropriate degree course, usually biomedical sciences at the university; if certain criteria are met students may be able to transfer onto the medicine degree at the same or an affiliated university. It is important to note that you should check carefully with the university before applying for a specific degree course that it is a possibility to transfer. The criteria often include achieving certain grades in the non-medicine degree in your first year. There are often a very limited number of spaces for inter transfers and there is no guarantee that starting on the required non-medicine degree will mean you will be allowed to transfer. Biomedical science courses are sometimes eligible for graduate entry to medicine courses. course.

—

GRADUATE COURSES

These courses are aimed at students who are applying for medicine in the penultimate year of their undergraduate degree or who have already finished an undergraduate degree. The specific graduate only courses are accelerated and last for four years compared to the normal 5-6 years for school leavers. Generally, the preclinical years of an undergraduate programme are condensed down to between one or one and a half years in a graduate programme. It depends on the university but they may ask for the degree to be science related, although this is not always the case. Graduates are still able to apply for the undergraduate 5 year course and can apply for a mixture of 4 year and 5 year courses in their 4 UCAS choices. It is important for graduates to look at finances for the A100 and A101 course as they vary.

Off UCAS Courses

These are medical programmes you can apply for without having to go through UCAS and use up one of your 4 spaces. Similar to applying to UCAS, there are often fees associated with completing the entrance exams and submitting your application. There are many more available than the ones listed below. It is vital to do your research beforehand and check (amongst other things):

- The language they are taught in
- The cost of tuition fees
- If the qualification is recognised by the GMC/in the UK
- If there are any extra steps or exams you need to complete in order to become eligible to work in the UK or

MALTA

Barts and the London offers the same 5 year undergraduate medicine programme taught in Malta. They also offer a foundation year over there. It is important to note that the tuition cost is higher than studying in England. The deadline for applications is much later: it was 1st May 2017 for the same year of entry. You are still required to sit the UKCAT. You apply directly to the university; you can apply for both the Barts course in London and Malta and if you are short-listed for both, you will do one interview in London.

IRELAND

There are six universities in Ireland that offer medicine courses (excluding Northern Ireland - Queen's University Belfast - for which you apply through UCAS). You will need to sit the Health Professions Admissions Test (HPAT) which has only one sitting (February) in Ireland. It is similar to the entrance exams used in the UK such as the UKCAT and BMAT. It is a 2 and a half hour test consisting of three sections: logical reasoning and problem solving, interpersonal understanding and non-verbal reasoning. You can also study for graduate medicine at specific Irish universities; students would need to sit the GAMSAT. You need to apply through the Central Applications office (CAO) which is their equivalent of UCAS (the website is www.cao.ie). The application deadline is the 1st Feb. You do not have to write a personal statement and there is no limit to the number of universities and courses you apply for. You will be offered a place based on your combined score from the HPAT and the Irish Leaving Certificate (or equivalent). There is no interview requirement. The Universities, and courses offered, are as follows:

- National University of Ireland, Galway offers undergraduate medicine
- Royal College of Surgeons in Ireland offers undergraduate and graduate medicine
- Trinity College of Dublin offers undergraduate medicine
- University College Cork offers undergraduate and graduate entry medicine
- University College Dublin offers undergraduate and graduate entry medicine.
- University of Limerick offers graduate entry medicine

CHARLES UNIVERSITY, PRAGUE

It has five independent faculties; three in Prague, one in Pilsen and one in Hradec Kralove that offer the medicine course in English. The degree takes six years. You apply directly to the faculties through their websites. There is also an entrance exam to complete.

UNIVERSITY OF MALTA

Undergraduate medicine course taught in English. The course is for international students only. Application is directly through their website. The deadline for applicants is 15th March.

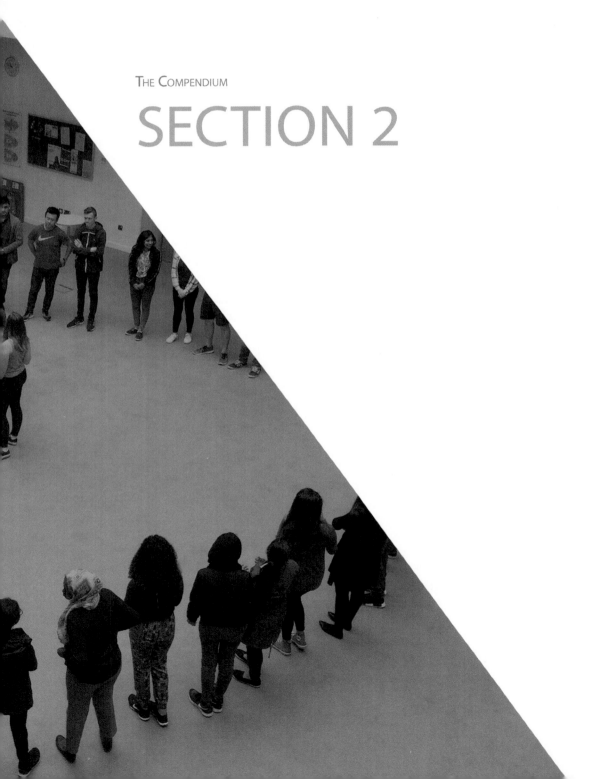

THE COMPENDIUM

SECTION 2

University of Aberdeen - School of Medicine

Contact Details

The School of Medicine, Medical Sciences and Nutrition, Polwarth Building, Foresterhill, Aberdeen, AB25 2ZD

E: medadm@abdn.ac.uk

T: 01224 437923

Courses Offered

A100

Background

Considered to be the first medical school in Scotland, founded in 1495, the Aberdeen Medical School includes its very own anatomy museum. The medical curriculum was revised significantly in 2009 and now offers a fresh, innovative approach to studying with high-class facilities and choice of study throughout the programme. The university is set close to the seaside, with neighbouring mountains so your extracurricular time can be spent in a multifold of ways.

Course Information

The course style is a systems-based, integrated approach, with a mixture of small group teaching and lectures. Students are taught the human physiology, anatomy and disease process accordingly to build understanding and knowledge.

Anatomy

Prosection with dissection opportunities offered in a minority of cases. However there is also a 3D anatomy resource to aid learning.

Intercalation

Offered after fourth year and students can apply externally to other institutions

Elective

8 weeks in fifth year and completed at any time throughout the year

Entry Requirements - A100

Entrance Exam

UKCAT: There is no minimum score cut-off, instead applicants are ranked relative to all applicants in that cy-

University of Aberdeen - School of Medicine

cle, with scores varying from 1200-3600 from the three UKCAT subsets. The SJT component is only used to make the decision of an offer when any two applicants score similarly.

In 2016, the minimum score for offer was 2480 and the maximum score for offer was 3350, with the minimum score for interview invitation being 2180.

A Levels

AAA at first sitting over 2 years: [1] chemistry compulsory, [2] then one of biology/ human biology, maths or physics, [3] plus another of choice, exceptions: general studies/ global perspectives and research. AS grades not used for interview selection.

International Baccalaureate

36 points required overall. At Higher level: Chemistry required, plus one of biology/ maths/ physics, plus one other. Standard level: 6 subjects at grade 6, chemistry required plus two sciences of biology/ maths/ physics, exception: maths studies.

Scottish Highers

Minimum AAAAB. National: English and maths grade B minimum, recommend biology and physics grade B minimum. Highers: Chemistry grade B minimum, two subjects from biology/ human biology/ maths/ physics - higher biology will prove particularly useful.

Welsh Baccalaureate

May be considered, we advise you to contact the admission office

GCSEs

At least grade C in english and maths. Biology and physics recommended. Grades A and B expected, especially in science subjects.

Graduates

Accepted onto undergraduate programme. Require at least a 2:1 degree with honours classification. Grade B A level or equivalent is required in chemistry, although may not be necessary if chemistry undertaken as part of the previous degree or alternative study in chemistry has been undertaken; this will be assessed on a case by case basis. Graduates are also required to sit the UKCAT.

If the degree taken is not with honours, candidates can apply as a mature application but must still have the Chemistry requirements.

Access Courses Accepted

Assessed on a case-by-case basis, advised to contact the admissions office.

Extra Application Information

- A levels resits: Modular resits accepted within the two year window, but whole A level resits outside of the two years will only be considered in cases of mitigating circumstances.
- UCAS reapplication: Can re-apply, but recommended that you obtain feedback as to why your application was unsuccessful to make improvements; no more than 3 attempts to apply, but each attempt up to a maximum of three will be considered. Each application is a clean slate.
- Deferred entry: Acceptable provided there is good reason and there is an objective intent, undertaking work or experience with a caring nature.
- Medical school transfers: Not offered
- Internal transfers: Not offered

Admissions Data

Number of applications: 2150
Number of interview places: 837
Total number on course: 178 (20)

Applications
Non-academic Requirements

Applicants require an excellent personal statement, evidence of commitment to medicine and need to be a team player. Attempts to experience, research and understand the role of a doctor are recommended; for example job shadowing with GPs or hospital doctors, talking to doctors, news and literature, research the university you are applying to. Applicants are also advised to undertake work of a caring nature (paid or unpaid), initiatives that help school colleagues and contribute to school life.

Interview Selection

[1] Academic score and [2] UKCAT score are combined to select candidates for interview. Overall for offers, 30% comes from academic, 20% from UKCAT and 50% from interview performance.

University of Aberdeen - School of Medicine

Interview Information

Multiple mini interviews, 7 in total for 7 minutes each, covering professionalism, team working ability, roles of a doctor, commitment to medicine and information provided on your personal statement.

Interview Season

November to February

Interview Outcome

End of March, at the end of the interview season

Accommodation - Guarantee of Halls

For first year, halls are guaranteed to all undergraduates; they are located 30 minutes walk away from the university.

Student Perspective

Unique Selling Points

- A modern, contemporary campus, that is close to the teaching hospital; overall this is one of the largest clinical teaching sites in Europe
- Study of medical humanities offered for 6 weeks and can be taken in languages, research, global health or public health and many more
- Aberdeen offers a unique remote and rural placement, where students can undertake emergency medicine in the wilderness

Things to Consider

- Accommodation can be expensive
- Small city
- Seagulls can be a pest

Aston Medical School

Contact Details

Aston Express Way, Birmingham, B4 7ET
E: medicalschool@aston.ac.uk
T: 0121 204 3284

Courses Offered

A100

Background

Aston is a brand new independent (private) medical school to open from 2018, set in the inner city of Birmingham. Aston will only be opened to international students but will designate a number of widening access to medicine places for home students. Currently, it is expected that students graduating from the University of Aston medical school will be able to proceed into the UK foundation programme. The Aston medical school will first open in September 2018 and therefore the curriculum is still being finalised and the following information may be subject to change, hence we would advise you to check the website. However this means a brand new curriculum designed for the 21st century is yet to be launched.

Course Information

A patient centred curriculum, focusing on translational medicine and science, developed in association with Leicester University. Core skills include: teamwork, NHS working, caring and compassion. The course comprises of lectures and small group tutorials.

Anatomy

Taught using a systems-based approach, using virtual methods and technology with plastinated models. There may be a limited number of prosection opportunities in the future.

Intercalation

Not offered

Elective

6 weeks at the end of fifth year

Entry Requirements - A100
Entrance Exam

UKCAT: No cut-off for the first year of applicants

Aston Medical School

A Levels
AAB, requiring chemistry and biology. Exceptions: general studies and critical thinking.

International Baccalaureate
Not accepted

Scottish Highers
Not accepted

Welsh Baccalaureate
Not accepted

GCSEs
5 at minimum grade B, including english language, mathematics, chemistry, biology or double science

Graduates
Will consider graduates with a 2:1 classification degree for the undergraduate programme.
Advised to contact the admissions team for further information.

Access Courses Accepted
Sir Doug Ellis pathway only, in association with partner schools in the Birmingham region only. Some foundation courses will also be accepted.

Extra Application Information
- Resits for A levels: A level resits accepted once. This may be more lenient if an applicant had mitigating circumstances whilst sitting their A Levels.
- UCAS reapplication: Please contact the institution's admissions department, as it is a new course for 2018.
- Deferred entry: Acceptable and advised to state in your personal statement your reasoning.
- Medical school transfers: Not offered
- Internal transfers: Not offered

Admissions Data
Number of applications: new course for 2018
Number of interview places: anticipate 300-400
Total number on course: 60 - 100 international students plus up to 20 students accepted from the Sir Doug Ellis widening access initiative from partner schools only in the Birmingham region.

Applications
Non-academic Requirements
At least two weeks of work experience in a care setting is expected. The personal statement must show evidence of:
- Interest in medicine
- A diverse skillsets and array of extracurricular interests/activities
- An altruistic nature
- Voluntary work is highly regarded
- Acquisition and development of communication skills
- Motivation and ability to work independently

Medical work experience is ideal but community and voluntary work is also valued, and a need to demonstrate continuity of commitment.

Interview Selection
On an individual case by case basis, assessing past experience and achievements from the personal statement and based on predicted grades, UKCAT will also be considered.

Interview Information
Multiple mini interviews, consisting of 7-10 stations to assess communication skills, problem solving, past experience according to personal statement, motivation, commitment and knowledge of 'medicine'.

Interview Season
December to March, requires a week VISA, no skype interviews accepted.

Interview Outcome
Contact the admissions department to check as the date has not yet been confirmed.

Accommodation - Guarantee of Halls
Halls guaranteed for first year students, range of accommodation options thereafter in Birmingham city centre.

Student Perspective
Unique Selling Points
- First to offer enhanced medicine and leadership component; awarded mini MBA in leadership and management

Aston Medical School

- BTEC considered: Distinction in single level 3, plus chemistry and biology, and consider some UK foundation programmes
- Brand new curriculum adopting innovative teaching methods

Things to Consider

- Brand new medical school and brand new curriculum so not tried and tested
- Caution: Awaiting GMC final stage approval
- This course is only open to widening access to medicine and international students

Barts and the London School of Medicine and Dentistry (Queen Mary)

Contact Details

Garrod Building, Turner Street, Whitechapel, London, E12AD

E: smdadmissions@qmul.ac.uk

T: 020 7882 8478 / 020 7882 2243

Courses Offered

A100

A101 (Graduate Entry)

The Barts Health Scheme - Foundation Programme

Background

Barts and the London Medical School is situated in East London. It has 3 main sites; Charterhouse Square in Barbican, Whitechapel and Mile End. The history of the medical school goes far back; St Bartholomew's Hospital opened in 1123 and The London Hospital Medical College is the oldest and first medical school in England and Wales and opened in 1785. In 1995, St Bartholomew's Hospital Medical College and The London Hospital Medical College merged with Queen Mary University.

Course Information

Problem based learning (PBL) sessions are weekly in pre-clinical years and are led by academics as well as lectures and computer assisted learning (CAL) sessions for histology and pharmacology. PBLs in the clinical years are led by doctors based in the hospital. In the clinical years there is a lecture based week before each new clinical placement. The course is taught as spiral curriculum, with the first pre-clinical year going over the healthy human body and the second pre-clinical year going over the disease state and what goes wrong.

Anatomy

Anatomy teaching is taught using prosections and surface anatomy sessions. Dissection of cadavers is optional on the A100 programme and is compulsory on the A101 programme.

Intercalation

It is optional and normally happens after 3rd year. It can be taken externally.

Barts and the London School of Medicine and Dentistry (Queen Mary)

Elective
6 weeks at the end of fifth year

Entry Requirements - A100
Entrance Exam
UKCAT: 2017 = 1731, 2016 = 2331, 2015 = 2670

A Levels
AAA (2017 results onwards) to include chemistry or biology, plus another science or maths (includes biology, chemistry, physics, or maths). It does not include critical thinking or general studies. AAAb (2016 results and before) three A levels and one AS level, with two science A levels from biology, chemistry, physics or maths. Both biology and chemistry at AS need to be at least grade B. If you have taken four A levels which includes two science and two non-science subjects , the offer is AAAC with A grades in biology or chemistry. Further maths is acceptable at AS level only, if both maths and further maths are taken.

International Baccalaureate
38 points, with 6 points in Higher level science subjects and 6 points in the third Higher level subject. Subjects to include chemistry or biology and one other science or maths at Higher levels. Three subjects at Standard level including biology or chemistry if not taken at the Higher level. English must be offered at grade B GCSE minimum if not taken at IB.

Scottish Highers
AAA in Highers to include biology and chemistry. AA in Advanced Highers in two of the subjects taken in Highers to also include chemistry and/ or biology.

Welsh Baccalaureate
Not accepted

GCSEs
AAABBB (777666 - iGCSEs) to include biology/ human biology, chemistry, english language and mathematics/ additional mathematics/ statistics. Science double award will count as a single science GCSE.

Graduates
Degree requirements are the same listed under A101.

Access Courses Accepted
None accepted

Entry Requirements - A101
Entrance Exam
UKCAT: 2017 = 1731, 2016 = 2331, 2015 = 2850

Degree
Upper 2:1 in any degree discipline. Must have a significant component (at least equivalent to AS level) of biology and chemistry in your degree. You will need to see if your degree meets the requirements of biology and chemistry content by using the degree title checker on the university website or by contacting the admissions office prior to application. If you have a bachelor of arts degree, you must meet the AS level requirements of BB in chemistry and biology (it can be completed prior to or after your degree). Degrees must be completed within the normal length intended e.g. 3 years for a bachelors degree.

Entry Requirements - The Barts Health Scheme (previously known as Newham Doc Scheme)
Widening access scheme for applicants studying/living within East London in the boroughs of Newham, Tower Hamlets, Barking & Dagenham, Hackney and Havering and Waltham Forest. First year of study is at Newham University Hospital with successful completion of this year allowing progress onto the five year A100 programme.

Application is through UCAS, although only students' teachers can put forward applicants for this scheme.

Entrance Exam
The UKCAT must be taken and applicants need to score more than the 3rd decile.

A Levels
Offer will be between AAB and BBB to include two science A levels from chemistry, physics, biology and maths with biology and chemistry both at B at AS level.

GCSEs
Maths and english language at grade C. Excluding criteria: you will not be eligible to apply to the scheme if you have already achieved your A levels or have met the requirements for the A100 programme.

Barts and the London School of Medicine and Dentistry (Queen Mary)

Extra Application Information

- Resits for A levels: Students must not haven taken more than 2 years to complete their A levels, unless they re-sat their AS or A Level and are protected under the Equality and Diversity Act 2010 (evidence will be required).
- UCAS reapplication: Can reapply with no limit to number of applications.
- Deferred entry: Applications are accepted for the A100 and A101 course if put on the UCAS form; they will then be assessed in the cycle in which they apply. Requests for deferred entry after the UCAS form was submitted will be looked at individually.
- Medical school transfers: Barts does not offer transfers to other medical schools for current students. It does accept transfers from Cambridge and St. Andrews.
- Internal transfers: Not offered

Admissions Data

Number of applications: A100 - 2500, A101 - 1500
Number of interview places: A100 - 800, A101 - 200
Total number on course: A100 - 253, A101 - 39
(24 spaces for international students across A100 and A101)
The Barts Health Scheme- 4

Applications
Non-academic Requirements

The university recommends that applicants have used work experience to explore what medicine entails. Volunteering in a caring role is valued equally to work experience in a clinical setting. The university may check work experience references.

Interview Selection

A100: ranking based on a 50:50 weighting between UKCAT score and academic ability (UCAS tariff). You will not be offered an interview if the total UKCAT score is below the third decile but, there is no guarantee that you will get an interview if it is above the third decile. Applicants are expected to be predicted a UCAS tariff of at least 144.

A101: Ranking based on a 50:50 weighting of UKCAT score and academic ability (points based on degree classification or postgraduate degrees).

Interview Information

Once you reach the interview stage, everyone is on an even playing field and the scores are based on how you perform during the day. The personal statement is not used to assess whether you get an interview, but may be used during the interview process. In both A100 and A101, the interviewers will check the applicant has an adequate amount and type of work experience.

A100: Interview panel which usually consists of senior academic or clinical staff (2), a medical student and sometimes a lay person (15-20 minutes). A case or topical issue will be sent out ahead of time and this will be discussed at interview.

A101:Selection centre involving a group-based task and a structured interview (half a day).

Interview Season

January to March

Interview Outcome

End of March

Accommodation - Guarantee of Halls

Halls are offered at Charterhouse Square and Whitechapel campus for medical students. Priority is given to students who live furthest away. You are unlikely to be offered accommodation if you live within commutable distance from the university unless there are extenuating circumstances.

Student Perspective
Unique Selling Points

- Barts and the London has its own student union, separate from Queen Mary University and is just for medical and dental students. You can join societies under both Barts and the London and Queen Mary University, which results in more societies on offer.
- The pre-hospital care programme is offered to undergraduate students alongside their studies to increase their experience of pre-hospital care. It was the first of its kind in the UK. It is in collaboration with the London Ambulance Service and London's Air Ambulance.
- There is also early introduction of OSCE (practical examinations) so you get really familiar with the examinations.

Barts and the London School of Medicine and Dentistry (Queen Mary)

Things to Consider

- Accommodation often offered in Charterhouse Square and lectures held in Whitechapel, which means a 20 minute commute on public transport.
- Accommodation is only with medical/ dental students and not mixed with students studying other subjects.

- Travel to placements can be quite far away, some placements are in Essex (although you will be often provided with accommodation).

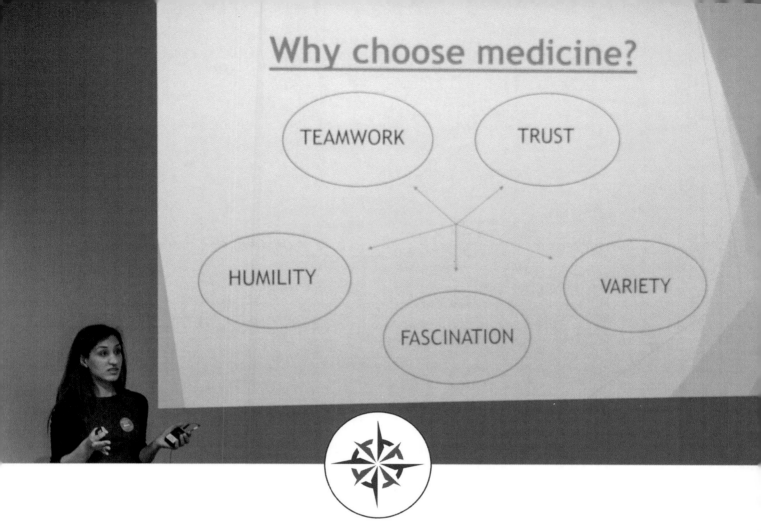

University of Birmingham Medical School

Contact Details

The Medical School, Edgbaston, Birmingham, B15 2TT

E: medicineadmissions@contacts.bham.ac.uk

T: 0121 414 3344

Courses Offered

A100

A101 (Graduate Entry)

Background

The Birmingham medical school is one of the largest and oldest medical schools in the UK, set in the beautiful town and greenery of Edgbaston; it is a campus university which embraces diversity and welcomes a student population of 27,000. The medical school is innovative and contemporary, designed with students in mind and the school is situated next to the state of the art Queen Elizabeth Hospital Birmingham, which opened its doors in 2010, hence equipped and designed for twenty first century medicine.

Course Information

The course style is an integrated modular programme, comprising of lectures, small group tutorials, plus elements of problem based learning and self-directed learning. The course equips students with the foundations in physiology, anatomy and biochemistry needed to appreciate the aforementioned in the context of disease, predominantly in the clinical years. The hospitals and trusts linked to the Birmingham medical school offer high quality clinical placements, with a diverse patient community, offering exposure to a broad array of pathology and disease, setting you up for your future career in medicine.

Anatomy

Monthly prosection with dissection opportunities offered in a minority of cases. However there is also a 3D anatomy resource to aid learning. There are weekly small group tutorial sessions and online anatomy resources are made available to students 24/7.

University of Birmingham Medical School

Intercalation
Optional and can intercalate after years 2, 3 or 4; a minority of students are permitted to intercalate externally

Elective
4-6 weeks at the end of year 4

Entry Eequirements - A100
Entrance Exam
UKCAT: There is no minimum score cut-off, instead applicants are ranked into deciles. The decision analysis is not considered in the ranking process. For 2015, applicants in tenth decile equated to a UKCAT score of <1120 whereas first decile applicants equated to a score of > 2980. The SJT component is used at interview.

A Levels
Predicted A*AA and achieve at least AAA requiring chemistry and biology/ human biology. Exceptions: general studies and critical thinking. AS grades are not used for interview selection.

International Baccalaureate
At least 32 points required overall. At Higher level: 766 from chemistry and biology and one other. Standard level: must include chemistry, bology, english and maths.

Scottish Highers
5 A grades in the Highers and AAB in Advanced Highers including chemistry and biology

Welsh Baccalaureate
Not considered

GCSEs
Numerical score given to GCSE grades for application process according to grade achieved and subject taken. The following subjects are scored: english language, english literature, maths, biology and chemistry (or dual), plus two subjects. Grade A*, A or B in these subjects will be scored in the ratio of 4:2:1 respectively. A maximum score of 7 can be attained.

Graduates
5-10 graduates will be accepted onto the undergraduate programme

Access Courses Accepted
- Access to Birmingham
- Routes to Professions
- Realising Professions

Entry Requirements - A101
Degree
All graduates require at least a high 2:1 degree classification with honours and historically a first class degree was preferred. Interview selection is based solely on the UKCAT.

A Levels
Typically AAA in biology and chemistry

GCSEs
Grades A/ B needed in english, sciences and maths, but there is no numerical grade academic score component, unlike for the undergraduate programme.

Extra Application Information
- Resits for A levels: Not considered, except in cases of mitigating circumstances. Can undertake modular resits within the two year A level window.
- UCAS reapplication: Will not consider any applicant who has previously been rejected following interview at the Birmingham medical school, otherwise can reapply.
- Deferred entry: Acceptable provided there is good reason and the year will broaden your experience; does not necessarily have to be healthcare related.
- Medical school transfers: Not offered
- Internal transfers: Only for students studying a health-related science course at the University of Birmingham and only after one year of study; please note this may no longer be available.

Admissions Data - 2015
Number of applications: A100 - 3017, A101 - 500
Number of interview places: A100 - 1000, A101 - 50
Total number on course: A100 - 334 (28), A101 - 40

Applications
Non-Academic Requirements
Candidates must demonstrate academic excellence, motivation to medicine and the core NHS values of a

University of Birmingham Medical School

doctor. Applicants should have undertaken people-focussed work experience or volunteering to demonstrate these latter qualities. Work or doctor shadowing is not required but instead evidence of active involvement in a healthcare environment, alongside extracurricular involvement to further develop these important skills is accepted. Although work experience is not a requirement, it is strongly advised to give insight into medicine.

Interview Selection

70% GCSE grades and 30% UKCAT, plus A level predicted grades and personal statement considered. Personal statement needs to demonstrate evidence of commitment, motivation and core values of a doctor. Following interview, where candidates are evenly matched, the decision for offer will be informed by GCSE grades attained.

Interview Information

Multiple mini interviews, 6 stations of 6 minutes each covering ethics, communication, work experience, data analysis, motivation for medicine and self-insight.

Interview Season

November to March

Interview Outcome

December: top 50% offers, bottom 20% rejected, then remaining pooled and same done in March

Accommodation - Guarantee of Halls

For first year, halls are guaranteed for all undergraduate students, just a 30 minute walk from the university.

Student Perspective
Unique Selling Points

- A modern, contemporary campus, that is next to a world-class, teaching hospital
- Birmingham medical school is gradually growing to become a European centre for research
- Birmingham is a diverse city of culture

Things to Consider

- Large cohort
- Logistical and administrative problems from time to time
- The anatomy component of the programme comprises a lot of self-directed learning so students must be proactive in this

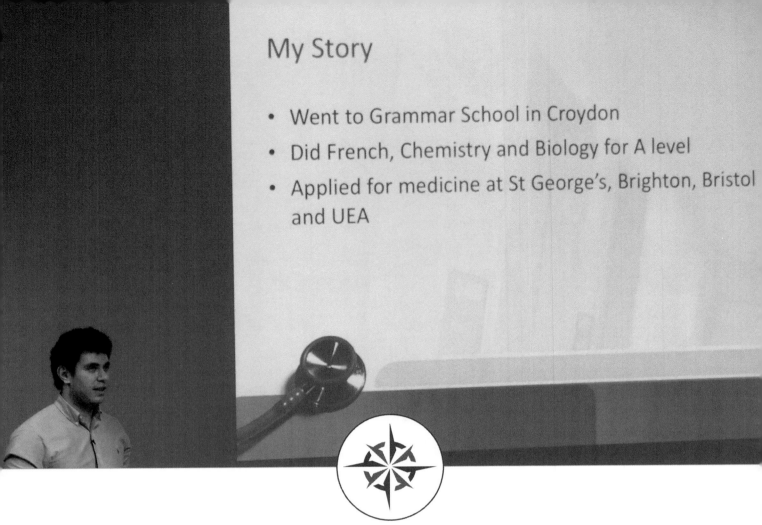

My Story

- Went to Grammar School in Croydon
- Did French, Chemistry and Biology for A level
- Applied for medicine at St George's, Brighton, Bristol and UEA

Brighton and Sussex Medical School

Contact Details

BSMS Admissions Registry, Checkland Building, Falmer Campus, University of Brighton, BN1 9PH

E: medadmissions@bsms.ac.uk

T: 01273 643528

Courses Offered

A100

Background

A medical school formed in 1997 through the partnership of the Universities of Brighton and Sussex, all-the-same, it has quickly become a very popular medical school. Brighton and Sussex offers a dynamic curriculum with a small cohort and high-quality teaching and facilities. The curriculum provides a multi-disciplinary approach to learning medicine and produces doctors adept to 21st century medicine.

Course Information

An integrated curriculum with a practical approach, comprising of lectures and small group tutorials, com-bining traditional methods of teaching with research and innovation. Early on in the curriculum, the teaching style is predominantly lecture-based, but throughout there is a focus on translating scientific learning into practice.

Anatomy

Full cadaveric dissection, offered weekly in years 1 and 2.

Intercalation

Offered subject to performance and normally after year 3, and can intercalate externally.

Elective

4 weeks at the end of year 5

Entry Requirements - A100
Entrance Exam

BMAT: 2016 requirement was approximately 17/28 and in 2015 requirement was 16.1/28 or higher, ranked from 28/28 downwards for interview selection.

Brighton and Sussex Medical School

A Levels

AAA - requiring chemistry and biology and prefer a third science. Exception: general studies.

International Baccalaureate

36 points required with chemistry and biology at grade 6 at Higher level

Scottish Highers

370 points with 18 united from 3 Advanced or (2 Advanced and 2 Highers) including chemistry and biology as Advanced Higher

Welsh Baccalaureate

AA in a level biology and chemistry, plus A in welsh baccalaureate and grade B at AS, excluding general studies

GCSEs

At least grade B in english language or literature and in maths

Graduates

Will consider graduates with at least a 2:1 classification degree for the undergraduate programme, provided they have a background knowledge of biology and chemistry from A level or degree studies. Alternatively graduates can apply via access to medicine scheme for mature students.

Access Courses Accepted

Regional access courses from local schools considered

Extra Application Information

- Resits for A levels: Will only be considered if grade drops one grade in one subject and applicant was originally predicted a grade A. Can resit modules in the two year A level window.
- UCAS reapplication: Can reapply with no limit to number of applications.
- Deferred entry: Can take a maximum of two gap years, provided this time is spent wisely and for good purpose.
- Medical school transfers: Not offered
- Transfers: if have completed one year of a health-related science degree at any other university, can apply to medicine at BSMS.

Admissions Data

Number of applications: 1500
Number of interview places: 450-500 (top 30% of applicants invited to interview)
Total number on course: 128 (10)

Applications
Non-academic Requirements

Personal statement should show evidence of reflection and demonstration of insight and understanding into medicine. Work experience in a healthcare e.g. hospital or GP setting, is not an absolute requirement but does help to give insight. Alternatively and/or in addition, students can undertake volunteering work in a care home or charity shop for example.

Interview Selection

Following screening of the academic attainment, selection is then based on the BMAT ranking, of which the top 30% are invited to interview. The personal statement is only used to assess international students and is not used in the application process for home or EU students.

Interview information

Multiple Mini Interviews, consisting of five discussions for 10 minutes each, in the format of question and answer around different scenarios, but there are no right or wrong answers.

Interview Season

January to March

Interview Outcome

March

Accommodation - Guarantee of Halls

Halls guaranteed for first year students.

Student Perspective
Unique Selling Points

- Strong sense of community between staff and students
- ePortfolio is provided throughout
- Can apply if completed 1 year of relevant degree at any other university

Brighton and Sussex Medical School

Things to Consider

- Students are expected to be well prepared for all small group tutorials and teaching sessions
- Students are encouraged to be self-directed in their learning and academic skills acquisition

- Preference given to a third science subject at A level or equivalent

Bristol Medical School

Contact Details

University of Bristol, Senate House, Tyndall Avenue, Bristol, BS8 1TH

E: choosebristol-ug@bristol.ac.uk

T: 0117 394 1642

Courses Offered

A100

A108 (Gateway to Medicine - Foundation Programme)

Background

Bristol is a renowned and well-established medical school, offering excellent teaching. The medical school is contemporary and modern and provides a diverse array of learning opportunities. The city of Bristol is a hub for music and arts, set by the seaside; it is very popular with the student population.

Course Information

A new and innovative curriculum is planned for launch in 2017. This will include the integration of clinical and basic science, interprofessional learning and research. The new curriculum focuses on health and wellbeing, with junior and intermediate clerkships and a senior assistantship, compromising of lectures, case-based learning, practicals and student directed learning throughout.

Anatomy

Anatomy is taught by prosection, with extensive learning opportunities and Bristol is considered to teach anatomy very well.

Intercalation

Offered after year 3 and can intercalate externally

Elective

8 weeks in year 5

Entry Requirements - A100

Entrance Exam

UKCAT: There is no minimum cut-off score and the SJT will not be considered

Bristol Medical School

A Levels

AAA, requiring chemistry and one other lab-based course. Exceptions: general studies and critical Thinking.

International Baccalaureate

36 points required overall, with 6 in chemistry and another lab-based subject at Higher level.

Scottish Highers

Advanced: AA in chemistry and another lab-based subject. Standard Higher: AAAAB.

Welsh Baccalaureate

Requirements are as for A levels where you can substitute a non-subject specific grade for the Advanced Welsh Baccalaureate Skills Challenge certificate at that grade.

GCSEs

Best 8 GCSEs considered. Minimum requirement of 5 GCSEs at grade A including maths, english language and two science subjects.

Graduates

Required to achieve at least a 2.1 Classification with AAB achieved at A level. Please note, Bristol no longer offer a graduate entry 4 year programme.

Access Courses Accepted

Considered on a case by case basis, advised to contact the admissions team

Entry Requirements - A108

The Gateway to Medicine programme is a widening access to medicine initiative at Bristol whereby 11 applicants, from a limited number of accepted schools/colleges (see website for the complete list of hundreds of schools, all ranked in the lowest 40%) will be accepted onto the Bristol foundation course, which consists of a foundation year of study and then entry onto the Bristol 5 year medicine programme. Please note this is not classed as a foundation course because entry requirements are stricter, particularly the contextual component. This course is designed for students who have the potential to become doctors but have not or cannot attain the grade requirements for entry onto the 5 year programme. Offers are based on typical and contextual requirements, the latter being the widening access

to medicine component. Applicants are assessed on an individual basis, but grade requirements are often two grades lower than for the 5 year programme.

UKCAT: Required and bursaries available to cover the cost.

A Levels

BBC in chemistry and another Science. Predicted grades of AAB or above are not eligible.

International Baccalaureate

29 points overalls with 5 in chemistry and 5 in another science at Higher level. IB with over 33 points are not eligible.

Scottish Highers

BB in biology and chemistry at Advanced and BBBBC at Standard level

Welsh Baccalaureate

You can substitute a non-subject specific grade for the Advanced Welsh Baccalaureate Skills Challenge Certificate at that grade

GCSEs

Grade B in double science, maths, english and another grade C in any other subject

Extra Application Information

- Resits for A levels: Can do 1 resit per subject in the two year window, but A level resits outside of the two year window will be accepted only in exceptional cases of mitigating circumstances.
- UCAS reapplication: Can reapply, but recommended that you obtain feedback; however each application is a clean slate.
- Deferred entry: Acceptable but must state in your personal statement what you plan to do. Deferred entry is not accepted for the A108 foundation course.
- Medical school transfers: Not offered
- Internal transfers: Not offered

Admissions Data - 2015

Number of applications: A100 - >3000
Number of interview places: A100 - top 20% of applicants
Total number on course: A100 - 236 (19), A101 - 11

Bristol Medical School

Applications
Non-academic Requirements
At least two weeks of work experience in a care setting. Personal statement must show evidence of interest in medicine, a diverse skillsets and array of interests/activities, altruism, voluntary work, communication skills, motivation and ability to work independently.

Interview Selection
Weighting consist of the following: 70% personal statement, 10% UKCAT, 12% A levels, 8% GCSEs and reference is read but not scored.

Interview Information
Multiple mini interviews, lasting 60 minutes in total, including assessment of data handling, practical tasks, communication station and a problem solving station.

Interview Season
November to April

Interview Outcome
Typically two - three weeks after the interview

Accommodation - Guarantee of Halls
For first year, halls guaranteed to all undergraduates

Student Perspective
Unique Selling Points
- Focuses on the arts in medicine
- Mentors provide valuable academic and social support
- Plenty of research opportunities are offered

Things to Consider
- New curriculum for 2017
- Students are encourage to be self-directed learners
- A competitive environment

University of Buckingham Medical School

Contact Details

Medical School, The University of Buckingham, Hunter Street, Buckingham, MK18 1EG
E: medicine-admissions@buckingham.ac.uk
T: 01280 827546

Courses Offered

A100 (4.5 years)

Background

Buckingham was the first independent medical school in the UK and is open to international students. Widening access places will become available once the first cohort have graduated in 2019 but currently, there are no widening access to medicine places available at Buckingham. Also, home students are unable to apply to the University of Buckingham medical degree. The 4.5 year programme is specially designed to train doctors for the demands of 21st century medicine.

Course Information

An integrated curriculum with guided learning through-out, designed from a well-established curriculum with 20 years' experience. The overarching focus of Buckingham is on the student experience and student satisfaction and hence student to staff ratios remain low to maximise learning. The curriculum consists of a modern and progressive format.

Anatomy

Anatomy is taught through virtual, digital resources including an anatomage table and 3D televisions. Anatomy TV is also available, plus a lot of models. Buckingham are in the process of accessing prosection specimens.

Intercalation

Not offered

Elective

7 weeks in year 5

Entry Requirements - A100
Entrance Exam

None required

University of Buckingham Medical School

A Levels

AAA, requiring chemistry and at least another science. Exceptions: general studies and critical thinking. At least grade B required at AS level.

International Baccalaureate

36 points required with chemistry and biology at grade 6 at Higher level

Scottish Highers

5 Highers needed, attaining AAABB including chemistry plus another science and two Advanced Highers including chemistry and another subject.

Welsh Baccalaureate

Accepted and considered as an equivalent to A level

GCSEs

8 grades A-C including biology, maths, chemistry, english

Graduates

Accepted onto the course, provided they offer a 2:1 degree classification

Access Courses Accepted

Considered on a case by case basis and if local to Buckingham, advised to contact admissions team for further information.

Extra Application Information

- Resits for A levels: No re-sits accepted.
- UCAS reapplication: Only if rejected due to insufficient academic requirements, any candidate rejected at interview will not be eligible for reapplication.
- Deferred entry: Only top 25-30% scoring applicants have the option to defer entry.
- Medical school transfers: Not offered
- Transfers: Not offered

Admissions Data

Number of applications: 500-600
Number of interview places: 160
Total number on course: 83
No cap on international places as an independent medical school.

Applications
Non-academic Requirements

Work experience is not a requirement

Interview Selection

[1] Academic selection: achievement at the highest level comparable to other medical schools' application criteria but applicants can offer a wide range of qualifications, then [2] objective structured selection examination: to assess personal skills and values. Work experience does not inform interview selection. The personal statement will be assessed whether the applicant appears as an ethical, honest and compassionate individual.

Interview Information

Multiple mini interviews, consisting of 8 stations of 7 minutes per station, to assess empathy and communication, understanding of medicine, numerical and analytical problem-solving skills, and ability to work as a team.

Interview Season

January

Interview Outcome

May

Accommodation - Guarantee of Halls

Guaranteed for all first year students.

Student Perspective
Unique Selling Points

- ePortfolio provided throughout
- Community feel and a focus on student experience; voted safest campus in the UK
- Start in January, not September

Things to Consider

- Not yet had a full programme run through and so the standard of doctors produced is currently unknown
- Currently no prosection or dissection facilities, and instead are reliant on technology and models teaching for anatomy
- Ability to defer depends on your academic standing, reapplication will not be considered if previously rejected from the University of Buckingham following interview and intercalation not offered

University of Cambridge - The School of Clinical Medicine

Contact Details
Cambridge Admissions Office, Fitzwilliam House, 32 Trumpington Street, Cambridge, CB2 1QY
E: admissions@cam.ac.uk
T: 01223 333308

Courses Offered
A100
A101 (Graduate Entry)

Background
Cambridge is a world leading scientific institute; ranked as the third best medical school in the world in 2016. It is located on site with the Cambridge Addenbrookes teaching hospital. Cambridge offers outstanding teaching in the beautiful setting of the cobbled streets of Cambridge. Cambridge exemplifies the elite and outstanding.

Course Information
The Cambridge course is taught in a traditional style, split into three years of preclinical and three years of clinical work; the amount of patient contact increases throughout the course. The course consists of 20-25 hours of scheduled teaching per week including a range of lectures, practical sessions and supervisions. The third year consists of the Biomedical science degree. Clinical studies, i.e. years 4-5, are undertaken at the Cambridge Addenbrooks teaching hospital.

Anatomy
Dissection, frequent opportunities and taught traditionally

Intercalation
Compulsory within 6 year course

Elective
7 weeks in year 5

Entry Requirements - A100
Cambridge uses a college system whereby applicants apply to a specific college rather than the University as

whole. The colleges share more similarities than differences so you should look at all the colleges available and see which may suit you best. The college system means that should applicants be unsuccessful from their first choice of college, they may be recommended to other colleges that may be better suited to the applicant. You cannot apply to both Oxford and Cambridge in the same year.

In addition to the UCAS application, students applying to Cambridge are required to complete a Supplementary Application Questionnaire, in which students are encouraged to supply their UMS scores for their modular examinations.

Please note: offers for applicants are very individual and tailored to the applicant following review of the application and interview.

Entrance Exam
BMAT: No cut-offs and no minimum scores.

A Levels
A*A*A: Chemistry and (one of biology/ human biology, physics, mathematics. (98% offer three or more sciences of which 30% get place). Applicants offering more than three A levels rank higher on the academic component.

International Baccalaureate
Applicants require a score of 40-42, achieving 776 in the Highers

Scottish Highers
40-42 points with 776 at Higher level

Welsh Baccalaureate
Three A level subjects offered as part of an Advanced Diploma, and the core may be used to assess applications and may contribute to an offer.

GCSEs
There is no GCSE cut-off but are used instead as a 'performance indicator'. Students are scored in the context of the type of school at which the GCSEs were undertaken, with ranking in decreasing order of state school, faith school and independent school. The majority of applicants have attained 4-5 GCSEs at grade A or A*'s, but Cambridge accept that post-16 performance is a superior measure and hence will consider applicants with excellent predicted grades in spite of a less excellent GCSE performance.

Graduates
Classed as affiliate students, can undertake the course in five years rather than six (pre-clinical takes two years rather than three) at one of the following colleges only: [1] Lucy Cavendish, [2] Hughes Hall or [3] Wolfson College.

Access Courses Accepted
Some colleges may accept access courses in exceptional circumstance but generally not accepted, advised to contact the admissions team and check the website.

Entry Requirements - A101
Graduates are able to apply to both the undergraduate and graduate entry courses provided that they apply to the same college for both. Also, unlike for undergraduates who can only apply to one college for Oxbridge in each application cycle, graduates can apply to more than one college in Oxbridge in any one application cycle.

Degree
At least a 2:1 degree in any discipline

A Levels
Grade A/A* in chemistry and AS or A level pass in two other sciences. However, AAA or above would be a competitive applicant.

GCSEs
Grade C in maths and double science or biology and physics.

For other qualifications, it is recommended that you contact the admissions team.

Extra Application Information
- Resits for A levels: Not accepted, even modular resits. Only in very exceptional circumstances colleges may accept extenuating circumstances but generally no.
- UCAS reapplication: Students can reapply but are

University of Cambridge - The School of Clinical Medicine

advised to apply to a different college the second time. There is no limit to the number of application, but again apply to different colleges and previous applications will not be considered, it is therefore a clean slate each time.

- Deferred entry: Offered and do not need to state your reasoning in the personal statement.
- Medical school transfers: Not offered
- Transfers: Not offered

Admissions Data

Number of applications: A100 >1000, A101 - 368
Number of interview places: A100 - 75% interviewed, A101 - 80% interviewed
Total number on course: A100 - 269 (20), A101 - 23

Applications
Non-academic Requirements

Applicants are strongly advised to undertake paid or voluntary work experience to gain an insight and understanding into medicine, but acknowledge that there are a wide range of ways in which this insight and skillsets can be attained. Hands on experience in patient care is preferable and ideally in an NHS setting. Applicants are expected to have a good scientific knowledge, with an inquisitive scientific nature. Please note: College specific requirements, see website: often require written work pre-interview.

Interview Selection

Every applicant who has a realistic chance of being offered a place to study medicine at the University of Cambridge is offered an interview. Interview selection is based solely on academic performance.

Interview Information

Applicants will have 1-3 interviews, of 20-45 minutes duration each; the style, length and number of interviews varies from college to college. The content of the interview is academically-orientated (scientific questioning) and relating to your experience. The interviews will test your ability to problem-solve, think outside the box and reason on the spot; Cambridge interviews are designed to challenge the applicant.

Interview Season

First three weeks of December, a minority are asked to return for a second interview in January

Interview Outcome

January to February

Accommodation - Guarantee of Halls

Guaranteed for all first year students and in most colleges offered for all years of the course.

Student Perspective
Unique Selling Points

- Opportunity to undertake an MBPhD
- World-leading institute
- Range of teaching methods

Things to Consider

- Strong work ethic expected and high academic requirements
- Supplementary questionnaires required in addition to UCAS application for admissions
- There are additional course costs for equipment etc.

University of Cardiff - School of Medicine

Contact Details

School of Medicine, Cardiff CF10 3XQ
E: medadmissions@cardiff.ac.uk
T: 029 2068 8113

Courses Offered

A100
A101 (Graduate Entry)
A104 (Foundation Programme)

Background

Cardiff is the oldest medical school in Wales dating back to 1893. The Cardiff medical school takes a large cohort and implements a case-based learning curriculum. The school is contemporary, focusing on international collaborations, whilst attaining a community approach.

Course Information

An innovative, spiral, integrated curriculum, grounded in sound scientific reasoning and developing an aptitude for research. However there are significant planned changes to the curriculum to be introduced in 2018. The course comprises lectures, small group teaching and significant amount of problem-based learning.

Anatomy

Cadaver dissection offered on a weekly-fortnightly basis

Intercalation

Offered after year 3 or 4, and can intercalate externally.

Elective

8 weeks in year 5

Entry Requirements - A100

Entrance Exam

UKCAT: There is no minimum score for consideration for interview. Offer threshold: 2016 = 2330, 2015 = 2310

A Levels

A*AA: including chemistry or biology and one other science. Exceptions: critical thinking, general studies, citizenship studies and foundation courses (full list on website).

University of Cardiff - School of Medicine

International Baccalaureate

Overall need 36 points not including theory of knowledge and extended essays. Applicants also need 19 points of Higher i.e. 7, 6, 6 from biology and chemistry and another subject.

Scottish Highers

'AAAAA' grades in Highers, including chemistry, physics, and biology, plus 2 Advanced Highers of AA including chemistry.

Welsh Baccalaureate

Grade A in the core of the Advanced Diploma, plus grades AA in chemistry and biology A levels.

GCSEs

Applicants must have attained the following GCSE grades: B english, B maths, A double science or AAB triple science, plus up to 9 GCSE's at grade B. GCSE resits are accepted if within 12 months of first sitting.

Access Courses Accepted

An ACCESS programme is open to mature students and applicants must send a CV and a reference; preference is given to applicants who have been out of education for more than four years.

Entry Requirements - A101

The Graduate A101 accelerated medicine programme at Cardiff is offered to students on feeder stream courses inclusive of the following: BMedSci Degree in Medical Sciences from the University of Bangor (B100), BSc (Hons) Medical Sciences Degree, from the University of South Wales (B901), BSc (Hons) Medical Pharmacology degree, School of Medicine, Cardiff University (B210), BSc (Hons) Biomedical Sciences degree, School of Biosciences, Cardiff University (BC97). This is a widening access to medicine initiative. However, graduates can apply for the 5 year programme provided they have a 2:1 or first class degree. Applicants must sit the GAMSAT admission test and must send a CV detailing their past experience.

A small number of students admitted to one of these aforementioned courses, accepted by the A101 programme, will be welcomed to enter into second year of the A100. This will be subject to academic and non-academic selection.

A Levels

Graduates or undergraduates must have an A level and/or degree in biology and/or chemistry, otherwise they will be required to apply for the foundation 6 year course. BBB is required where applicants from the feeder courses wish to apply for medicine

GCSEs

Grades B in english language and maths, where applicants from the feeder courses wish to apply for medicine For all other qualification requirements, students are advised to contact the admissions office.

Entry Requirements - A104

Entrance Exam

GAMSAT: 57 required overall with 55 achieved for the sciences.

A Levels

AAA attained. This course is designed for students who do not have the correct subject specialisms, rather than students who have failed A levels.

Scottish Highers

Please contact university for further details

Welsh Baccalaureate

Grade A plus two A level subjects

GCSEs

As for A101

Extra Application Information

- Resits for A levels: Accepted if sat within the two year A level window. In the case of mitigating circumstances, applicants will be assessed on an individual basis as to whether resits will be accepted.
- UCAS reapplication: Can reapply with no limit to number of applications.
- Deferred entry: Accepted but outline in your personal statement the reasons why.
- Medical school transfers: Not offered
- Transfers: Not offered

Admissions Data

Number of applications: A100 - 3500
Number of interview places: A100 - 1500

University of Cardiff - School of Medicine

Number of places: A100 - 309 (25), A104 - up to 50 students, A101 - up to 100, from one of the four feeder courses onto medicine

Applications
Non-academic Requirements
A range of factors are assessed by the admissions team when deciding whether to call a candidate for interview including academic results, extracurricular attainment, socioeconomic background and the applicants appreciation of Welsh culture, language and society. Applicants' communication skills, ethics, sense of responsibility, drive for medicine and work-life balance will be assessed for consideration of interview and offers.

Interview Selection
Applicants are assessed firstly based on their academic results, then their personal statement and their reference. UKCAT is only used as a decider after interview if any two candidates are evenly matched.

Interview Information
Multiple mini interviews format, consisting of ten stations lasting 6 minutes each. The aim of the interviews to assess the applicant's aptitude, values and skillset to determine if they are suited to a career in medicine.

Interview Season
November to January

Interview Outcome
February/March - Rank all applicants and only then give offers

Accommodation - Guarantee of Halls
Guaranteed for full-time first year students

Student Perspective
Unique Selling Points
- 73% of the course is offered in Welsh
- ERASMUS Exchange: Successful students can choose to study the women, children and family placement at one of their partner medical schools in France, Spain, Portugal and Italy.
- You will be provided with a stethoscope

Things to Consider
- Independent learning can be challenging
- Large student cohort
- Transport links are sometimes limited

Dundee Medical School

Contact Details

Ninewells Hospital & Medical School, Dundee, Scotland, UK, DD1 9SY

Online form: http://medicine.dundee.ac.uk/contact

T: 01382 384697

Courses Offered

A100

A101 (Graduate Entry run in conjunction with St.Andrews University - for details look at St.Andrews)

A104 (Gateway to Medicine - Foundation Year)

Background

Dundee medical school opened 50 years ago but has become popular with students very quickly, given its innovative and patient-centred approach to studying medicine. Dundee medical school is set alongside a modern clinical teaching hospital and the focus throughout is on the provision of high quality teaching and producing excellent graduates.

Course Information

The Dundee curriculum is of a spiral nature, with inter-locking phases, body system based and innovative approach, which is student-centred and community based. Dundee boasts a 21st century curriculum.

Anatomy

Dissection, with multiple opportunities per semester

Intercalation

Yes, selection based on academic attainment and CV and completed after year 3. Students can also intercalate externally.

Elective

8 weeks in year 4

Entry Requirements - A100
Entrance Exam

UKCAT: There is no minimum score for consideration for interview. 2013 offer threshold = 2720

Dundee Medical School

A Levels

AAA: including chemistry or biology and one other Science, third subject does not have to be science-related. Exceptions: Critical thinking, general studies, citizenship studies and foundation courses (full list on website).

International Baccalaureate

Minimum of 37 points with three grade 6 at Higher level including chemistry, plus another science. Also need three Standard level subjects at grade 6.

Scottish Highers

AAAAB: Chemistry and another science, plus need three Advanced Highers including chemistry

Welsh Baccalaureate

Not accepted

GCSEs

Applicants need to have attained a grade B in english, maths and sciences.

Graduates

Can apply to the undergraduate programme, requiring at last a 2:1 degree.

Access Courses Accepted

None accepted

Entry Requirements - A104

This course is not a foundation course but is designed for either widening access students or students who do not have a scientific background.

For widening access to medicine students, one of the following contextual factors must be met:
- One of the 20% most deprived home postcodes in Scotland
- From your college, a progression rate of <20% attained
- Past experience of care, either provided or received
- An asylum seeker of refuge
- Subject to significant mitigating circumstances that prohibited meeting full potential.

A Levels

AAB including chemistry and one other science

Scottish Highers

AABB including chemistry and one other science

GCSEs

Will be considered but no absolute requirements

For Applicants with a Non-science Background

For 'very able' candidates but who have no scientific background, although attainments in non-science subjects have been equivalent to those expected to be achieved by A100 candidates for the A100 programme.

A Levels

AAA excluding chemistry and includes up to one other science only

Scottish Highers

AAAAB excluding chemistry and up to one science only

International Baccalaureate

37 points overall required with 6, 6, 6 attained in Higher level, excluding chemistry and including up to one science only. Also 3 subjects at Standard level all at grade 6.

Graduate Entry

2:1 degree classification required

UKCAT is required in both cases

Extra Application information
- Resits for A levels: Not accepted, except in cases of mitigating circumstances. A level modular resits are also not accepted but can resit GCSE's outside of the two year window.
- UCAS reapplication: Maximum of two UCAS applications, will look at previous applications and want to see improvement.
- Deferred entry: Accepted provided the year will be useful to your personal and/or professional development.

Admissions Data

Number of applications: A100 - 1700

Number of interview places: A100 - 600

Total number on course: A100 - 160 (13), A104 - 15 (widening access students). Ring admissions for number of places for non-scientific background students.

Dundee Medical School

Applications

Non-academic Requirements

Dundee encourages applicants to undertake two weeks of healthcare-related work experience to gain insight into a medical career; work experience is considered essential by the University of Dundee. Applicants are expected to have knowledge of medicine, demonstrate dedication and motivation to study medicine, show evidence of leadership and ability to work in a team. Extracurricular activities, contributing to your community and competitive achievements in sport are also highly regarded.

Interview Selection

For interview selection, 60% is comprised of academic attainment and the remaining 40% is from the UKCAT score. The personal statement is only used at interview, not for initial selection.

Interview Information

Multiple mini interviews format, consisting of ten stations lasting 6-7 minutes each. The individual stations can be of two forms either [1] one to one questions with your interviewer, where you may be presented with a situation of dilemma, asking you to think critically and on the spot, and [2] working with a role player to see your communication skills. The interviews are designed to challenge the applicant and test how you work under pressure. Once applicants are selected for interview, there is a clean slate and candidates are then only ranked according to interview performance to determine offers.

Interview Season

December to January

Interview Outcome

March

Accommodation - Guarantee of Halls

Guaranteed for first year students

Student Perspective

Unique Selling Points

- Small community with a focus on the student experience
- Fantastic facilities and teaching hospital
- Can reapply after interview rejection

Things to Consider

- No A level resists considered at all, including modular resits
- Will consider previous applications to Dundee if reapplying and need to see improvement
- Welsh baccalaureate not considered

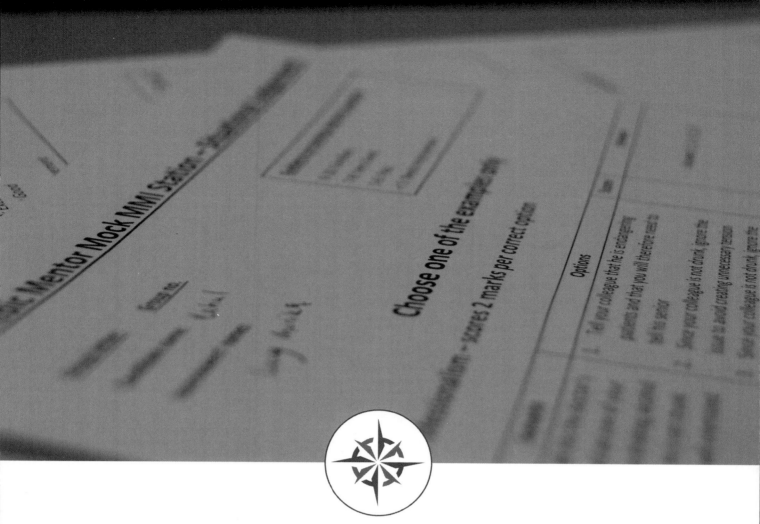

Edinburgh Medical School

Contact Details

University of Edinburgh-The Queen's Medical Research Institute, 47 Little France Cres, Edinburgh EH16 4TJ

E: medug@ed.ac.uk

T: 0131 242 6407

Courses Offered

A100

Background

Edinburgh medical school was established in 1726, but medicine was taught in Edinburgh long before this formal establishment, with the Barber surgeons! As one of the first English speaking medical schools, the school arose out of the 'Scottish enlightenment' period. With excellent teaching, Edinburgh is a highly regarded medical school, set in a city of culture and arts that is vibrant and historic.

Course Information

The Edinburgh curriculum is progressive and systems-based, delivered in a traditional manner. The first two years are preclinical with a limited amount of patient-contact, the third year is the research BSc year and then the remaining three years are clinical. A range of teaching methods are used including lectures, small group teaching, self-directed learning and problem-based learning, with an underlying scientific focus.

Anatomy

Taught using prosection and virtual cadavers

Intercalation

Compulsory - as within the six year programme

Elective

8 weeks in year 5, can be split into two blocks of 4 weeks

Entry Requirements

Entrance Exam

UKCAT: There is no minimum cut-off and all scores will be considered for selection. Then applicants are ranked and divided into octiles. Thereafter, UKCAT may be used as a decider between evenly scoring candidates.

Edinburgh Medical School

Maximum and minimum scores for offers:
2016: 2370-2850, average=2850
2015: 2330-3290, average=2822
2014: 2520-3530, average=3049

A Levels

AAA including chemistry and one other science plus a grade B at. Third subject does not have to be science-related. Exceptions: Critical thinking, general studies, citizenship studies and foundation courses (full list on website).

International Baccalaureate

Minimum of 37 points achieving 6, 6, 7 at Higher level including chemistry, plus another science. Also need three Standard level subjects at grade 6 including biology.

Scottish Highers

AAAAB: including chemistry and two other sciences, preferably completed by S5 but if missing one science subject can take this in S6.

Welsh Baccalaureate

Not considered

GCSEs

Applicants need to have attained a grade B in english, maths and sciences

Graduates
Degree

At least a 2:1 degree

Scottish Highers

BBBB in S5

A Levels

BBB
High quality science qualifications are expected, advised to contact the admissions office to check eligibility.

Access Courses Accepted

Only the following access courses are accepted:
- College of West Anglia Access to Medicine Course
- Sussex Downs Adult College Access to Medicine Course

Extra Application Information

- Resits for A levels: Not accepted, except in cases of mitigating circumstances. Will accept a maximum of two A level modular resits within the two year window only.
- UCAS reapplication: Can only reapply if rejected due to lack of qualifications, if rejected for any other reason, candidates will not be reconsidered.
- Deferred entry: Offered and do not need to include details in your personal statement.
- Medical school transfers: Not offered
- Internal transfers: Not offered

Admissions Data

Number of applications: >2000
Number of interview places: Only shortlisted mature and graduate applicants are interviewed. Undergraduate applicants do not have an interview.
Total number on course: 210 (10)

Applications
Non-academic requirements

The expected personal qualities include good communication skills, empathy and interpersonal relationships. Work experience is recommended to gain an insight and understanding into medicine, such as shadowing and talking to doctors; the focus is on quality as opposed to stipulating a length of time. Applicants are also expected to attend for an open day. Candidates must demonstrate a range of non-curricular involvement and activities.

Interview Selection

For interview selection, 50% is comprised of academic attainment, 30% is from the non-academic requirements and 20% from the UKCAT.

Interview Information

Undergraduate admissions applicants are not interviewed. Only mature or graduate applicants will be expected to attend for interview, in which case the interview will be 35 minutes split into three ten minute sessions with two interviewers. The interview focuses on ethics, communication skills and insight into medicine. Shortlisted applicants will be provided with communications and ethics questions and given 20 minutes to prepare their answers, which will be discussed during the interview.

Edinburgh Medical School

Interview Season

Rolling basis

Interview Outcome

March

Accommodation - Guarantee of Halls

Guaranteed for all first year students

Student Perspective

Unique Selling Points

- No interview required
- Established curriculum with excellent teaching
- Vibrant city of culture

Things to Consider

- Compulsory six year programme
- Expected to attend for open day if want to apply

University of Exeter Medical School

Contact Details

University of Exeter Medical School, St Luke's Campus, Heavitree Road, Exeter, EX1 2LU

E: medicine@exeter.ac.uk

T: 01392 725500

Courses Offered

A100

Background

Set in beautiful, tranquil Exeter, the campus university is green and idyllic. Exeter was previously called Peninsula medical school and was joined with Plymouth but both medical schools are now separate schools. The medical school has clinical placements across Cornwall, giving students a far-reaching scope of experience.

Course Information

A broad-based curriculum, comprising of lectures and small group teaching, focussing on patient-centred education. The course comprises an integrated problem-based learning style.

Anatomy

Use life-simulated models, no cadavers are used

Intercalation

Offered usually after year 4 and can intercalate externally

Elective

At least 4 weeks at the end of year 5

Entry Requirements - A100
Entrance Exam

UKCAT: Minimum cut-off each year. In 2017, 2000 was the requirement for offers (as there were fewer sections) but in 2016, 2250 was the cut-off for offers.

A Levels

A*AA-AAA, including biology and chemistry at grade A. Exception: General studies

International Baccalaureate

Applicants need 36-38 points, including grade 6 in chemistry and biology at Higher level

University of Exeter Medical School

Scottish Highers
At least five Scottish Highers at AAAAB and three Advanced Highers at AAB with grade A in chemistry and biology

Welsh Baccalaureate
Accepted: Require grade A in chemistry and biology at A level also

GCSEs
At least grade C in english and maths

Graduates
Applicants are required to take the GAMSAT and to achieve 59 to be considered for interview.

Access Courses Accepted
No access courses are accepted, but do offer outreach sessions in the local region

Extra Application Information
- Resits for A levels: Can retake A level modules in the two year window and GCSE's outside of the two year window.
- UCAS reapplication: Can reapply with no limit to number of applications.
- Deferred entry: Accepted, you should state reasoning in your personal statement.
- Medical school transfers: Not offered
- Internal transfers: Not offered

Admissions Data
Number of applications: 1817
Number of interview places: <400
Total number on course: 130 (10)

Applications
Non-academic requirements
Work experience is not a requirement

Interview Selection
Based solely on academic attainment and provided applicants have met the minimum UKCAT cut-off. Then UKCAT is used as a decider following interview. Personal statements are not scored.

Interview Information
Multiple mini interviews format, consisting of 7 stations of 3 minutes length each. The stations are one-to-one interviews and focus on communication skills, evidence of empathy, good reflection and assessing for the core principles of a doctor.

Interview Season
December to February

Interview Outcome
January to February, only give offers after all candidates interviewed

Accommodation - Guarantee of Halls
Guaranteed for first year students

Student Perspective
Unique Selling Points
- Beautiful campus with a sense of community and good support for students
- Innovative teaching curriculum, combining theory and clinical experience
- New medical imaging suite

Things to Consider
- The cohort is split up in third year where half of students go to Truro
- A lot of self-directed learning, independent learning which can be challenging, especially with anatomy
- High entry requirements with no access courses accepted

Glasgow Medical School

Contact Details
Medical School Office, University of Glasgow, Glasgow G12 8QQ01392 725500
E: med-sch-admissions@glasgow.ac.uk
T: 0141 330 6216

Courses Offered
A100

Background
Glasgow is an evolving city and the medical school is one of the largest in Europe. The medical school has an impressive history dating back to the 17th century and being renowned for Joseph Lister and William Hunter to name a few. A purpose built medical school was opened in 2002.

Course Information
The curriculum consists of lectures, problem-based learning and case-based learning, and is spiral in nature allowing for topics to be revisited in increasing depth as students progress through the course. There are four phases in total starting with biomedical science, the second and third are systems-based modules and then the fourth is entirely clinical with academic days. Glasgow are renowned for pioneering teaching methods and good facilities.

Anatomy
Anatomy is taught using virtual methods

Intercalation
Offered usually after year 3 and can intercalate externally

Elective
Two electives of 4 weeks each at the end of year 3 and 4

Entry Requirements - A100
Entrance Exam
UKCAT: There is no minimum cut-off but applicants are ranked. Minimum for interview: 2016 = 2680, 2015 = 2630

A Levels
AAA chemistry and one other science. Exceptions: General studies, critical thinking, global perspectives.

Glasgow Medical School

International Baccalaureate

Applicants need 38 points, including grade 6 in chemistry and biology and either maths or physics

Scottish Highers

Applicants can attain either AAAABB or AAAAA in the Advanced Highers. Chemistry, biology and another science are required i.e. maths or physics at Highers level and english must be provided at grade B from the Standard level or equivalent.

Welsh Baccalaureate

Not accepted

GCSEs

At least grade C in english and maths

Graduates

Applicants are required to take the GAMSAT and to achieve 59 to be considered for interview

Access Courses Accepted

Glasgow work with 95 partner schools with priority postcodes to widen access to medicine

Extra Application Information

- Resits for A levels: Can retake A level module resits in the two year window but no GCSE resits will be considered and only A level resits outside of the two year window in cases of exceptional circumstances.
- UCAS reapplication: Can reapply with no limit to number of applications.
- Deferred entry: Accepted but do not need to state reasoning in your personal statement.
- Medical school transfer: Can transfer externally if either personal reasons or if would otherwise have met Glasgow entry criteria or are performing academically well at their original university.
- Internal transfer: Not offered

Admissions Data

Number of applications: 2000
Number of interview places: 600-700
Total number on course- 230 (18)

Applications

Non-academic requirements

Work experience is not required for an offer but applicants should demonstrate commitment to caring through paid or voluntary work for example.

Interview Selection

Interview selection is based on the following: academic attainment, personal statement and reference and then UKCAT score.

Interview Information

The interview lasts for 30 minutes and consists of two panels of two interviewers, including scenario-based discussion. The interview focuses on insight, commitment, enthusiasm, communication skills, experiences, your achievements and skills, reflection and your personal statement.

Interview Season

December to March

Interview Outcome

March - offers are only given after all candidates are interviewed.

Accommodation - Guarantee of Halls

Guaranteed for first year students

Student Perspective

Unique Selling Points

- The institution makes improvements based on student feedback
- The range of teaching methods is effective
- Two elective experiences across two different years

Things to Consider

- Very independent learning required and the lectures vary in quality
- Some organisation problems
- Hospitals can be old-fashioned

Hull York Medical School

Contact Details
John Hughlings Jackson Building, University of York, Heslington, York YO10 5DD, UK
E: admissions@hyms.ac.uk
T: 01904 321782

Courses Offered
A100

Background
Hull York medical School opened in 2003 and is part of the University of York, a city which boasts beautiful architecture and character. Hull York medical school has quickly gained its reputation for innovative teaching.

Course Information
The course offers a balance of teaching as a spiral curriculum, comprising of lectures, small group tutorials, with lots of time spent in primary care; the course is very patient-centred. The course is comprised of problem-based learning also.

Anatomy
Predominantly case-based anatomical study, with a minority of students receiving dissection experience

Intercalation
Can intercalate after year 2 or 3 and can also intercalate externally

Elective
7 weeks at the start of year 5

Entry Requirements - A100
Entrance Exam
UKCAT: no minimum cut-off rank. Hull York consider the national average score and for all applicants scoring above this or equivalent to this level, they would be considered for interview however applicants falling below this will not be considered. (Please note the national average score can be found on the UKCAT website in October and changes year on year)

Hull York Medical School

A Levels

AAA, in 2 years, including biology and chemistry. Exceptions: General studies, applied science, citizenship or critical thinking. Hull York encourage students to study an arts subject as well, as their third A level. Mitigating circumstances considered. A level resits are acceptable, provided within the two year A level window.

International Baccalaureate

Applicants must have achieved 36 points overall and 6, 6, 5 at Higher level, including biology and chemistry.

Scottish Highers

Minimum AAAAB at Higher level, including biology and chemistry at grade A. Also need A grades in biology and chemistry in Advanced Highers plus a third subject at grade A. National: need grade B in english and maths, advise grade B in biology and physics. Highers: Need chemistry grade B and then advise two sciences.

Welsh Baccalaureate

AA in biology and chemistry and grade B in pass in the core, plus a third A level at grade B, excluding general studies and critical thinking.

GCSEs

Applicants need 8 GCSEs at grade A*-C or equivalent, or grades 4-9 in the reformed GCSEs. English language and maths at GCSE grade B or above, or reformed GCSE grade 6 or above (with a pass in spoken english), or equivalent. Best GCSE's considered but please note if the above criteria are not met the candidate will still be considered.

Graduates

Accepted onto undergraduate programme. Require at least a 2:1 degree classification with honours predicted or achieved. Applicants need a relevant science background either from A levels or degree.

A Levels

ABB, need chemistry and biology grade A (or can be made up for if a science degree was undertaken)

GCSEs

Require 8 GCSEs at grades A*-C
UKCAT required
Applicants with SJT Band 4 will not be considered

Access Courses Accepted

Assessed on a case by case basis, advised to contact the admissions office. Please note Hull York medical school actively supports widening access to medicine.

Extra Application Information

- Resits for A levels: Accepted provided modules are sat in the two year window.
- UCAS reapplication: Can reapply with no limit to number of applications.University advises applicants to seek feedback if unsuccessful.
- Deferred entry: Applicants can defer. Reasoning not needed in the personal statement.
- Medical school transfers: Not offered
- Internal transfers: Not offered

Admissions Data

Number of applications: 1000
Number of interview places: 560 - 600
Total number on course: 141 (11)

Applications
Non-academic requirements

At least one week of clinical work experience is recommended, but the focus is on the quality of the experience and the reflection as opposed to the length of the experience. Commitment to medicine can also be demonstrated through long-term volunteering.

Interview Selection

Based on GCSE ranking and UKCAT score; although they state that 40% of the weighting is comprised of the UKCAT score, the UKCAT is the greatest decider because candidates often all have excellent GCSE grades. Contextual information is also taken into account for example where you live and your parents' education. The personal statement is not scored and is only used to rule out 'red-flags'.

Interview Information

The interview consists of multiple stations; there are two 10 minute semi-structured interviews with two interviewers including three key questions which the candidate is asked to give reasoning for. There is also a scenario-based station with an actor; this is not designed to test medical knowledge but rather your communication manner for 5 minutes. There is also a group interview for

Hull York Medical School

20 minutes. The personal statement is not used in the interview.

Interview Season
January to March

Interview Outcome
Complete all interviews and only then give offers

Accommodation - Guarantee of halls
Guaranteed to all first years

Student Perspective
Unique Selling Points
- 1 in 2 get an offer following interview and there is an excellent online applicants guide
- Year groups are small so it is nice to get to know everyone and the university focuses on the student experience
- Nice to belong to two institutions, best of both worlds for expertise and teaching etc.

Things to Consider
- Problem based learning can be challenging to gauge your knowledge and understanding
- Entry criteria change quickly
- Belonging to two campuses may not suit everyone

Imperial College - School of Medicine

Contact Details

Level 2, Faculty Building, South Kensington Campus, London SW7 2AZ, UK

E: medicine.ug.admissions@imperial.ac.uk

T: 020 7594 7259

Courses Offered

A100

A101 (5 Year Option for Graduate Entry Students)

Background

Imperial College medical school was established in the nineties and today reflects a world-class institute with campuses based across London; medicine is taught at four campuses around London. It is one of the largest medical schools and is internationally renowned for its programme, which has a distinct research focus. Set in the hub of London, there is an array of culture, diversity and social life.

Course Information

Research technique and methodology focused with a strong scientific emphasis throughout and on communication skills. The course comprises of lectures, tutorials, problem based learning, laboratory classes, computer workshops, clinical demonstrations and seminars. The first two years are science focused, third year is clinical, fourth year is a BSc and the final two years are clinical.

Anatomy

Dissection offered weekly in first and second year, then with student-shared dissection opportunities for the remaining duration of studies.

Intercalation

Compulsory component of the Imperial medical degree

Elective

6-9 weeks at the end of year 5

Entry Requirements - A100
Entrance Exam

BMAT: 2016 minimum scores: section 1 = 4.5, section 2 = 4.5, section 3 = 3.5

Imperial College - School of Medicine

A Levels

At least AAA and typical offer: A*AA, requiring chemistry and biology. Exceptions: Vocational, general studies and critical thinking. AS grades not used for interview selection.

International Baccalaureate

Typically 38 points required overall, with grade 6 in chemistry and biology

Scottish Highers

Advanced Highers AAA including chemistry and biology, the third subject does not have to be a science

Welsh Baccalaureate

Not accepted

GCSEs

No longer GCSE grade requirements

Graduates

If attained 2:1 or above, can apply for five year programme, otherwise would need to apply for six year MBBS

Access Courses Accepted

None accepted

Entry Requirements - A101
Degree

Applicants require a 2:1 BSc or a pHd for entry in a relevant biological sciences course including: Biochemistry, cell biology, physiology, bioengineering, biomedical science, pharmacology, but this is not an exhaustive list. In selection for interview, both academic attainment and BMAT will be considered as well as demonstration of the appropriate values for a doctor.

Entrance Exam

BMAT: There is no minimum cut-off score but applicants are ranked and previous years scorings may be considered relative to each cycle.

2017: section 1 = 4.5, section 2 = 4.6, section 3 = 2.5 and Grade B

Extra Application Information

- Resits for A levels: Can resit modules in the two year window.
- UCAS reapplication: Yes, can reapply, after first attempt.
- Deferred entry: Acceptable but must state in your UCAS application what you plan to do.
- Medical school transfers: Not offered
- Internal transfers: Not offered

Admissions Data

Number of applications - A100: >2000, A101: >600
Number of interview places - A100: 750, A101: 90
Total number on course - A100: 320 (20-30), A101: 20

Applications
Non-academic Requirements

Applicants need to demonstrate evidence of commitment, motivation, community engagement/involvement, team working, leadership and extracurricular activities. Applicants are required to have work experience; quality over quantity is considered, but 1-2 weeks would be considered reasonable. Alongside this, a demonstration of continued interest and commitment to medicine must be shown.

Interview Selection

Academic attainment and prowess is the most important deciding factor. [1] BMAT, [2] A levels, plus referee's report and [3] personal statement values

Interview information

Panel interview of 15 minutes with a chairperson, 2 panel members and a senior medical student, plus a lay observer. Assessment areas include: Commitment to medicine, insight into the field and how you will contribute to imperial medical school life.

Interview Season

December to March

Interview Outcome

Offers are made on a rolling basis and candidates will hear very shortly after interview

Imperial College - School of Medicine

Accommodation - Guarantee of Halls

For first year, halls offered to all undergraduates

Student Perspective

Unique Selling Points

- Course is well-structured, where although each year is different, the expectations and requirements are made apparent
- A world class institute in an amazing location

- A research focused programme

Things to Consider

- Expectation of strong work ethic, with high competition for entry: 7 applications per place
- Expensive to live in London and travelling out to placements can be challenging
- 6 year course with compulsory BSc

Keele University - School of Medicine

Contact Details
School of Medicine, Medicine CUG award 2017, David Weatherall building, Keele University, Staffordshire, ST5 5BG

E: medicine@keele.ac.uk

T: 01782 733937

Courses Offered
A100

A104 (Foundation Programme)

Background
Keele University is campus-based and set in the beautiful heart of Staffordshire. Established in 1978, Keele remains a popular choice with students given the universities' beautiful setting and the innovative teaching curriculum.

Course Information
The curriculum is modern, spiral in nature and highly integrated. It also incorporates an additional research pathway. However there are significant planned changes to the curriculum to be introduced in 2018. The course currently comprises of lectures, small group teaching, problem based learning and practical sessions.

Anatomy
Cadaver dissection, weekly in the first two years

Intercalation
Offered after year 2, 3 or 4 and can intercalate externally

Elective
8 weeks in year 5

Entry Requirements - A100
Entrance Exam
UKCAT: Minimum accepted score for consideration is 1630 but 20% of the lowest scoring applicants nationally and/or where SJT is in band 4, these applicants will not be considered for interview or offer.

2016 offer threshold = 2330

2015 offer threshold = 2310

2014 offer threshold = 1960

Keele University - School of Medicine

A Levels

A*AA: including chemistry or biology and one other science. Exceptions: critical thinking, general studies, citizenship studies and foundation courses (list on website).

International Baccalaureate

Applicants require a score of 35 points from six subjects. At Higher level, chemistry or biology needed, plus another science plus another rigorous subject.

Scottish Highers

Applicants need to have attained at least 5 subjects at grade A/ 1 including chemistry, biology, maths, physics and english language at grade B/2. At Higher or Advanced Higher level, applicants need AAAA of which two must be sciences i.e. chemistry, biology, maths and physics, but chemistry or biology must be offered at Advanced Higher level.

Welsh Baccalaureate

Applicants need an A* or A in A level chemistry plus at least another science

GCSEs

Applicants need at least 5 subjects at grade A, and grade B attained in maths, english and sciences

Graduates

Degree

2:1 or first class degree

A Levels

Applicants must also have attained grades BBB in chemistry or biology and another science, including statistics

GCSE

Grade B in maths, sciences and english language are also required

GAMSAT

All graduates must sit the GAMSAT and applicants must have achieved a combination of 55 overall and 58 in section 3 or, 58 overall and 55 in section 3. In both cases, applicants must have attained at least 50 in all sections.

Access Courses Accepted

- College of West Anglia (Distinction in all units)
- Stafford College (Distinction in all subjects)
- Sussex Downs College (Distinction in all units)
- Manchester College (Distinction in all areas)

Entry Requirements - A104

This course is open to students who not meet the entry criteria for direct entry into their chosen healthcare course, including medicine, e.g. students who have not studied sciences beyond GCSE level, or equivalent. The course consists of academic and personal development tuition and guidance, communication skills development and healthcare subjects, including medicine-related modules. To proceed onto medicine, students must have attained 70% in all modules, however this course offers progression onto a range of healthcare vocational courses. The course has been running for 10 years and has generated a total of 20 doctors.

Entrance Exam

No admissions test required

A Levels

A*AA attained within two years, not including chemistry but can include biology as the only science A level taken.

International Baccalaureate

Overall 35 points attained, with 6, 6, 6 at Higher level including chemistry and 6, 6, 5 and Standard level, including english at Grade 6

Scottish Highers

AAAAB not including chemistry and no more than one science, although physics and maths are acceptable if with another non-science subject

Welsh Baccalaureate

A*A at A level and grade A pass in the Welsh qualification, not including chemistry and with only one other science.

GCSEs

Grade A in 5 subjects and at least grade C in english and maths

Keele University - School of Medicine

Graduates

Degree

Non-honours degrees will be accepted if attained over 70%. For honours degrees, classification must be at least 2:1 in a non-science subject.

A Levels

BBB minimum

GCSEs

Grade C in english and maths

Extra Application Information

- Resits for A levels: Accepted but must wait until you have your final grades before applying, i.e. applicable if resitting and/or A levels take more than two years to complete. GCSE resists can be undertaken and modular resists for A levels are accepted, within the two year window.
- UCAS reapplication: Can reapply provided that you have not been interviewed previously.
- Deferred entry: Can defer entry but must state in your personal statement your reasoning.
- Medical school transfers: Not offered
- Transfers: Not offered

Admissions Data

Number of applications - A100: 2000, A104: 250

Number of interview places - A100: 500, A104: <100

Total number on course - A100: 129 (will significantly increase from 10% from 2018), A104: 10

Applications

Non-academic Requirements

Applicants are required to complete a 'Role and Responsibilities' form to outline details of work experience undertaken and to assess your aptitude for medicine (see website for full details). Work experience is important to gain insight into medicine, and hands-on, in-depth experiences are preferable to allow reflection. There is also a focus on team work and maintain a healthy work life balance with regards to academic studies and extracurricular activities.

Interview Selection

Applicants are screened based on their academic results and UKCAT. Then applicants are ranked according to the 'Roles and Responsibilities' form regarding work experience undertaken and their reference is also considered; widening participation is an important consideration in Keele applications.

Interview information

Multiple mini interviews format, ranging from panel interview to role-play stations and problem solving. The MMIs aim to assess communication skills, empathy, ethics, resilience and understanding of medicine and the role of the doctor.

Interview Season

December to March

Interview Outcome

February at the earliest

Accommodation - Guarantee of Halls

Accommodation not necessarily guaranteed for first year students

Student Perspective

Unique Selling Points

- Interprofessional group activities
- Lecturers are keen to help their students
- Cheap living costs set in modern facilities and a green campus

Things to Consider

- Clinical placement travel distance can be far

King's College London - Medicine

Contact Details

Strand, London WC2R 2LS

Online form: https://www.kcl.ac.uk/study/undergraduate/apply/enquiry-form.aspx

T: 020 7848 7890

Courses Offered

A100

A101 (Foundation Programme)

A102 (Graduate Entry)

Background

King's College London is a renowned university set in the centre of London on a beautiful campus and is one of the largest medical schools. An integral component of the King's medical curriculum is interprofessional learning and teaching. King's offers a variety of elective opportunities with partner institutions across the world.

Course Information

The King's curriculum has undergone drastic overhaul and will therefore be significantly different for incoming students. The programme is innovative and integrative, offering a combination of tutorials, learning from patients and online resources to assist learning. A range of lectures and seminars are offered, plus small group and case-based teaching.

Anatomy

Cadaver dissection, frequently

Intercalation

Offered after year 2 and 3 and can intercalate externally

Elective

8 weeks in year 5

Entry Requirements - A100
Entrance Exam

UKCAT: There is no minimum cut-off score. The overall average from the four sub-tests is considered as opposed to individual sub-test scores and the SJT is used for short-listing candidates. King's recommend an average score of 600 to be competitive (2016: 630-650).

King's College London - Medicine

A Levels

A*AA: including chemistry and biology but no preferences for the third A level. Exceptions: General studies, critical thinking, thinking skills and global perspectives.

International Baccalaureate

Applicants require a score of 35 points and 7, 6, 6 at Higher level requiring chemistry and biology

Scottish Highers

AAA in Higher and AA in Advanced Higher in preferably chemistry and biology offered at Advanced or one of these subjects can be offered at Higher level only, both grade A's. English and maths are required at Standard level grade 1 or 2.

Welsh Baccalaureate

Previously accepted in place of an 'AS' level but from 2018 A*AA from A levels will be required

GCSEs

Grade B required in english and maths

Graduates for A100

Require grade B in chemistry and biology at A level: AAA is not a requirement for graduates applying to the A100 programme. Graduates must have an upper 2:1 degree classification but a lower 2:1 degree is accepted if a Masters at merit level is offered in combination with this degree class. If biology or chemistry were sufficiently covered in the degree, A levels in these subjects may not be required but advised to contact the admissions team for confirmation.

Access Courses Accepted

Access to medicine courses are accepted and no preference is given to any particular course. Advised to contact the admissions tutor to check for eligibility.

Entry Requirements - A101 (Foundation Course)

Designed for students studying A levels at a non-selective state school in the Greater London area or students who are partaking in 'Realising Opportunities' England.

A Levels

AAB-AAA requiring biology and chemistry and exclusions as for A100

Scottish Highers

Not accepted

International Baccalaureate

Applicants require 35 points overall and 6, 6, 6 in three Higher level subjects including chemistry and biology, However, if applicants have scored highly in the UKCAT, a minimum IB of 33 points will be considered. Grade 5 in Standard level is required in english and maths (or grade B's at GCSE would be equivalent).

GCSEs

Require english and maths at grade B

Eligibility criteria:

- Undertaking A levels at a non-selective state school
- Since age 11 years, you attended non-selective state schools and the list of your schools must be included in your UCAS application
- Taking an access to medicine course or completed such a course, achieving 60 credits overall, 45 credits at level 3, 36 level 3 credits at distinction and the remaining 9credits at merit
- UKCAT
- Evidence of commitment to your community in your UCAS application and personal statement
- Demonstrate enthusiasm, commitment and the capability to study medicine, and who will positively contribute to the Kings College London community

Special considerations when:
- In care
- Attended sixth form college ranked in bottom third
- Participating in Realising Opportunities or Kings access to medicine programmes

Selection and interviews are as for the A100 programme

Entry Requirements - A102 (Graduate Course)

Graduates can apply to both the A100 and the A102 in one cycle to maximise their chances of admission

Degree

Please note for 2018 entry onwards, your science degree must be in biosciences specifically. Upper 2:1 in a science degree or lower 2:1 degree and a merit at Master in science will be accepted. For diplomas in higher education of nursing or allied health care courses, a 2:1 classification is required plus grade A at chemistry A level.

King's College London - Medicine

A Levels

Requirement depends on nature of course. Only needed if undertaken an allied health course. If taken biosciences, A levels not considered.

GCSEs

No specific requirements

UKCAT

As for A100

Extra Application Information

- Resits for A levels: Modular A level resits are accepted but A level resits outside of the two year window will only be considered subject to mitigating circumstances. GCSE resits will only be considered in cases of mitigating circumstances.
- Re-application: Can reapply and no limit to number of applications.
- Deferred entry: Can defer entry but must state in your personal statement your reasoning.
- Medical school transfers: Possible for graduates who have studied for three years at the University of Oxford and then wish to undertake three clinical years at King's College London, advised to contact the admissions team for further information. It is also possible to transfer to Kings from another medical school.
- Internal Transfers: Not offered

Admissions Data

Number of applications - A100: 4000
Number of interview places - A100: 1000
Total number on course - A100: 300 (30), A101: 50 (Greater London Applicants) 5 (Realising Opportunities Applicants), A102: 28

Applications

Non-academic Requirements

Applicants are expected to provide evidence of commitment to and understanding of a medical career. Work experience is expected in a caring environment and/or observation in a healthcare setting. Where this is not possible, transferable skills and communication development in other settings will be considered. Applicants are expected to be team-players, who have contributed to their society e.g. school life and can demonstrate a good work life balance. Any scholastic activity is accepted and community involvement is a very desirable criterion and who have attained in extracurricular activities such as music or sport.

Interview Selection

Applicants are assessed on GCSE (or equivalent performance), predicted or achieved A-level grades (or equivalent), the UKCAT score, the personal statement and the reference. The academic score and the UKCAT score form the predominant assessment criteria.

Interview information

Multiple Mini Interview style, comprising of question and answer stations based upon medical scenarios, stations assessing personal; values needed for medicine and a data handling station. There will also be an ethical scenario station and a station to assess your understanding of medicine and what the career entails. All of the stations will be assessing your communication skills. However content for the A102 MMIs will differ.

Interview Season

January to March

Interview Outcome

Early May once all candidates have been interviewed

Accommodation - Guarantee of Halls

Accommodation not necessarily guaranteed for first year students.

Student Perspective
Unique Selling Points

- Beautiful campus set in the heart of London, attached to the top hospitals in England
- Excellent facilities, world class teaching, a prestigious reputation and is internationally recognised.
- Excellent elective facilities

Things to Consider

- Cost of living in London
- Large Cohort
- New curriculum and is still evolving

Lancaster Medical School

Contact Details

Lancaster Medical School, Lancaster University, Lancaster, LA1 4YW
E: medicine@lancaster.ac.uk
T: 01524594547

Courses Offered

A100
A900 (Foundation Year)

Background

Lancaster medical school is not only one of the newest medical schools to establish, but also one of the smallest with an intake of under 60 students per year, starting from 2006. There is a brand new Faculty of Health and Medicine, which provides modern facilities. Although an emerging institution, Lancaster aspires for great quality teaching, resources and research.

Course Information

The Lancaster medical programme is predominantly PBL style with tutorials and early clinical exposure.

Anatomy

Dissection

Intercalation

Optional between year 4 and year 5

Elective

4 weeks at the end of year 5

Entry Requirements – A100

Entrance Exam

BMAT: Introduced as part of the selection process in 2015/16. The total BMAT score is used by combing the score for section 1,2 & 3. Range for applicants invited to interview in 2015/16 was 9.7-16.4. (Some applicants with a lower BMAT score were invited to interview if they were already guaranteed one or they had mitigating circumstances during the BMAT)

A Levels

AAA (b in fourth AS level) if a fourth AS level was taken or EPQ. A*AA if no fourth AS level or EPQ.

Lancaster Medical School

A2 levels to include chemistry and biology.

Only one of maths or further maths will be counted.

Applicants who have taken three years to achieve their A levels will be considered if they achieved a minimum AAB/ABB on their first attempt. If there are mitigating circumstances, all AS and A2 levels must still be at a minimum grade C. There must be mention of taking another year to complete A levels in your personal statement and a reflection on their circumstances.

International Baccalaureate

36 points to include a minimum of 6 points at Higher level in biology, chemistry and a third subject. A minimum of 5 points is needed at Standard level in three subject. Applicants who have taken longer than 2 years to achieve the necessary points in IB will still be considered. A reflection on this must be included in your personal statements.

Scottish Highers

AAAAB at Highers to include biology and chemistry at A grade. AA at Advanced Highers in biology and chemistry. Applications will be considered if students have had to re-take Advanced Highers.

Standard Grade (Credit)/Intermediate 2/National 5 (Scotland)

Seven subjects to include biology, chemistry, physics, english language and maths. The required grades for Standard grade (credit) are 1 or 2, Intermediate 2 A or B and National 5 A or B.

Welsh Baccalaureate

Advised to contact the admissions team for consideration

GCSEs

Nine GCSES with at least a score of 15 points from them: A*/A=2 points, B= 1 point

Applicants who have already achieved AAA at A level or 36 points in IB to include biology and chemistry may be considered even if they achieved 12-14 points at GCSE. Minimum grade B in biology, chemistry and physics (core and additional science accepted), english language and maths.

Other GCSEs must be at minimum grade C.

Graduates

Upper 2:1 (transcript marks of more than 65%).

If the degree is a biological, biomedical or health science subject then BBB plus b in fourth AS level is required at A levels.

If the degree is any other subject then AAB plus B in fourth AS level is required at A levels with grade A in biology and chemistry.

General studies and critical thinking will be considered for the 4th subject.

GCSE requirements are the same as for school-leavers. If the applicant has less than 15 points then they will be expected to show exceptional achievement in their A levels and degree.

Access Courses Accepted

Access to Higher Education (Medicine) from Wirral Metropolitan, Southport, Manchester College and Sussex Downs College. Also accepted is the Staffordshire Access to HE Course (Medicine and Health Professionals), Foundation Year in Clinical Sciences from Bradford University and the Pre-medical studies course (Foundation Year) at Lancaster University.

Distinction or equivalent in the approved Access to Medicine Course.

Minimum of 5 GCSEs at grade B to include biology, chemistry and physics (core and additional science are accepted), English Language and maths.

An access to medicine course will not be accepted if the applicant has re-taken A levels and failed to meet the academic requirements the second time.

Lancaster University Widening Participation Scheme

Residential summer schools are run for students who meet the Widening Participation criteria. Select students from the summer school will be guaranteed an interview if they apply to the programme.

Entry Requirements - A900

Aim is to allow for successful progression onto the A100 programme.

Eligible if

- Not studying the required A levels for the A100 programme
- Must demonstrate a record of excellent achievement in GCSEs and A levels

Lancaster Medical School

- A levels should not include both biology and chemistry, but can include one of these subjects.
- Studying the required A levels listed under the A100 programme but have mitigating circumstances (check the website for what would be considered) that have had a serious impact on your A level grades.
- Must demonstrate a record of excellent achievement in GCSEs and have evidence of mitigating circumstances that have/had an impact on A level grades. In most situations, the university recommends you re-sit your A levels and then apply for the A100 programme.
- Studying the required A levels listed under the A100 programme but are not predicted the A level grades and attended a school/college where the results are below average in England (state-funded schools). Check for criteria for schools/colleges on the website and the admissions team are happy to confirm.
- Must demonstrate a record of excellent achievement in GCSEs and A levels compared to the average results of the school/college you are at.

Extra application information

- Resits for A levels: Applicants taking longer than 2 years to achieve A level grade requirements will be considered if GCSE and non-academic criteria are met. AAB/ ABB must have been achieved on first attempt in absence of mitigating circumstances. Otherwise all AS and A2 levels must be at least grade C.
- UCAS reapplication: Not considered if unsuccessful after interview in previous cycle. If rejected prior to interview and can evidence further growth e.g. additional work experience, then applicants can reapply.
- Deferred entry: Acceptable and do not need to justify in your personal statement
- Medical school transfers: Not offered
- Internal transfers: Not offered

Admissions Data

Application numbers - A100: 550-1600
Interview - A100: 200
Number of places - A100: 54 (4)

Applications
Non-academic Requirements

Work experience that will show that you have an understanding of a medical career, suitability and the right career path. Evidence of commitment to society which includes a caring role where you volunteer/work to help others.Applicants invited to interview must be prepared to provide contact details for proof regarding work experience/ volunteering mentioned in personal statement.

Interview Selection

Applicants who meet the academic entry requirements are then ranked on their BMAT score. Personal statements will be assessed for non-academic entry requirements and those candidates who meet these requirements as well as having a competitive BMAT score will get an invite for interview.

Interview information

MMIs: 12-15 stations, normally lasting 5 minutes each. An additional 20 minute station will be a group task. Interviewers at the stations include clinical staff, GPs, patients, members of the public, university staff and medical students. Scores will be added from all the stations and those with the highest total scores will be offered a place on the programme.

Interview Season

January to February

Interview Outcome

March

Accommodation - Guarantee of Halls

Guaranteed accommodation for first year students

Student Perspective
Unique Selling Points

- A small medical school so there is more staff contact and hence more valuable teaching
- The student support available is great, plus there is a great sense of community
- An affordable city

Things to Consider

- PBL is a key component of the course, which can be challenging
- University is not so aesthetically pleasing
- Divided into 9 colleges, which are self-catered residences of up to 900 people per college; the college systems means you miss out on meeting other students

University of Leeds - School of Medicine

Contact Details

School of Medicine, Worsley Building, University of Leeds, Leeds, LS2 9NL
E: study@leeds.ac.uk
T: 0113 343 2336

Courses Offered

A100

B991 (Foundation in Clinical Sciences of Medicine at the University of Bradford, 1 year)

Background

Founded in 1831, Leeds medical school has a longstanding reputation, with patient-contact throughout. Many pioneering medical and surgical advances have originated in Leeds such as the first dialysis and the inventino of the clinical thermometer. State-of-the art facilities supports students to learn from world-class academics.

Course Information

Leeds is a spiral curriculum with a broad-research agenda and an integrated systems-based approach. The curriculum is designed to challenge and is based on professional values and core themes, which are integrated throughout the five years. The course consists of lectures, small group teaching and practical sessions with a very minimal problem-based learning component, however the self-directed learning nature of the course increases progressively across the five year programme.

Anatomy

Full body dissection-offered in first semester but mainly in the second semester of year 1

Intercalation

Can intercalate after year 2 or 3 and in a minority of cases after year 4. Applicants can also intercalate externally.

Elective

6 weeks at the start of year 5

Entry Requirements - A100
Entrance Exam

BMAT: There is no BMAT minimum cut-off, but the score

University of Leeds - School of Medicine

comprises approximately 35% of the weighting for interview selection. The BMAT is used for undergraduates and graduates. Please note the UKCAT and GAMSAT although used before, are no longer the required entrance exams.

A Levels
AAA - including chemistry. Exceptions: Critical thinking, general studies, citizenship studies and state that there is no advantage to having four A levels.

International Baccalaureate
Applicants need 35 points overall, with grade 6 achieved in 3 subjects, including chemistry at Higher level. Also need two additional sciences at Higher or Standard level.

Scottish Highers
AAAAB at Higher level and AB at Advanced level including grade A attained in chemistry

Welsh Baccalaureate
Still require 3 grade As at A level

GCSEs
At least 6 grade B GCSEs with preference given to: english language, maths, double science or chemistry and biology

Graduates
Must offer a 2:1 honours degree and at least grade B in chemistry at degree level or at A level, otherwise must show evidence of education up to this level with an alternative qualification

Access Courses Accepted
Access to Leeds scheme and the Bradford collaborative programme

Entry Requirements B991 - University of Bradford
This is a widening participation opportunity for entry into Leeds medical school. Applicants are required to submit an additional form detailing their eligibility when applying.

There are three routes of entry:
1. Can enter into year 1 if then wish to go onto study a medically-related degree
2. If you do not have science A levels or requirements for year 1 BSc of Clinical Science, then can continue Clinical Science BSc or onto a health-related programme
3. Applicants fulfil the widening participation criteria and the academic and non-academic requirements, so students can enter into medicine at Leeds.

A Levels
Two subjects required at Grade C

GCSEs
English, Maths, Biology and Chemistry or double award science at Grade C

Eligibility Criteria:
- You are the first generation to undertake university education
- <£30000 per year gross income
- Eligible for 16-19 bursary
- Free school meals year 10-13
- Your schools' GCSE performance was less than the national average for attaining 5 GCSEs
- Currently or have lived in local authority care
- Group 4 – 8 according to standard occupational classification 2010 metrics for the highest earner in the family
- Live in an area that has low progression to higher education

Extra Application Information
- Resits for A levels: Will be accepted in exceptional cases of mitigating circumstances and in the case of an applicant who was given an offer from Leeds and missed one A level requirement by one grade. GCSE and A level modular resists are also scrutinised and will only be accepted in cases of extenuating circumstances which will need to be provided.
- UCAS reapplication: Yes, and it is a clean slate.
- Deferred entry: Yes but encourage a gap year spent in employment, volunteering or travelling, but reasoning does not need to be included in the personal statement.
- Medical school transfers: Considered on a case by case basis and individuals must be in good academic standing.
- Internal transfers: Offered for 20 students from the BSc in Clinical Sciences at Bradford University to transfer to the Leeds medicine programme.

University of Leeds - School of Medicine

Admissions Data

Number of applications - A100: 2000

Number of interview places - A100: 550

Total number on course - A100: 219 of which international (18), B991: 20 (from the foundation BSc)

Applications

Non-academic Requirements

Applicants for medicine are expected to have a range of non-academic outside interests, which can be personal to the candidate. Applicants will be required to complete a form detailing work experience and volunteering work details and contact information.

The applicants' interest and motivation for medicine will be assessed as well as the following skills: interpersonal skills, insight, social and cultural awareness and responsibility.

Interview Selection

Selection for interview is based on academic score, i.e. past GCSE grades or AS level grades (whichever are best so 9A* GCSE would be equivalent to AAA at AS level), predicted grades, plus BMAT score. The personal statement and reference are only screened and not scored. Following selection, interview performance only determines offers.

Interview information

Multiple mini interviews format, consisting of 8 stations for 7 minutes each. The stations may be scenarios based or consider information in your personal statement.

Interview Season

January to February

Interview Outcome

February - March

Accommodation - Guarantee of Halls

Halls guaranteed for first year students

Student Perspective

Unique Selling Points

- Extent of patient contact is considered a differentiating feature
- The exams are multiple choice questions only, no essay assessments
- The city is friendly and a hub of activity and there is a good sense of community

Things to Consider

- Strict resitting rules
- Organisational problems at times

Leicester Medical School

Contact Details

University of Leicester Medical School, Maurice Shock Building, PO Box 138, University Road, Leicester, LE1 9HN
E: med-admis@le.ac.uk
T: 01162522969 / 01162522966

Courses Offered

A100
A199 (Foundation Programme)

Background

Leicester medical school has been around for 40 years. A brand new dissection room opened in 2016 and a new £42 million build is underway to provide advanced facilities for medical students. The foundation year programme is new with the first cohort starting in September 2017.

Course Information

The course is taught through an equal balance of small group learning and problem-based learning, alongside lectures. Modules are allocated a certain day of the week for a term, for example Mondays would be respi-ratory and Tuesdays would be gastroenterology. Each term looks at different set of modules. All modules have a workbook for you to work through in the group work sessions.

Anatomy

Full body dissection is compulsory during the pre-clinical years

Intercalation

Intercalation is optional after the 3rd year and you can intercalate externally

Elective

8 weeks after finals in 5th year

Entry Requirements
Entrance Exam

UKCAT: No minimum UKCAT score to get an interview- it forms part of the selection with equal weighting alongside academic grades. Rejection if you get band 4 in situational judgement test

Leicester Medical School

A Levels

AAA to include chemistry and biology (biology can be taken to AS level). Critical thinking and general studies are not included. Maths and further maths are not counted as two separate subjects. They only accept foreign language A levels if the language is not the applicant's native tongue. 4th AS or EPQ may be used in a tie-break before or after interview.

International Baccalaureate

36 points to include chemistry and biology at Higher level. Grade 6 needed in all subjects.

Scottish Highers

AAA in Advanced Highers to include chemistry and biology. Can be in combination with A levels. Highers are not considered.

Welsh Baccalaureate

Accept grade A in the Welsh Baccalaureate qualification instead of a third A-level. A level chemistry and biology are still required at grade A.

GCSEs

Minimum grade C in english language, maths and two sciences

Graduates

Upper 2:1 degree in any discipline. Will not accept a second degree, Masters or PhD instead of a 2:1 or 1:1 in your first degree. Minimum grade B in two science GCSEs or equivalent. Minimum grade C in english language and maths.

Access Courses Accepted

Access to medicine course distinction with 45 level 3 credits at distinction accepted from the following places:
- City & Islington College
- Glasgow Kelvin College
- Lambeth College
- The Manchester College
- Stafford College/New College Telford
- Sussex Downs College
- College of West Anglia

It will not be accepted in lieu of A levels or poor A level grades in undergraduate or graduate applicants. Access to medicine applicants need to submit a full CV to include all academic qualifications, employment and explanations of any gaps, to be submitted before 15th October.

Entry Requirements - A199
Eligibility Criteria

Students who have lived and studied A levels/ BTEC in the East Midlands for the last two years. Must either be currently in year 13 or have left within the last two years prior to the start of the degree.

Widening Participation Requirements

Must meet both criteria in group A and one from group B
Group A
- Live in a neighbourhood with low participation in higher education (postcode in quintile 1 or 2 in POLAR3 young participation- check postcode on http://www.hefce.ac.uk/postcode/
- GCSEs taken at a non-selective state school

Group B
- Have been/are in local authority care/ looked after. Evidence will be needed from the local authority
- Household income of no more than £35,000. Evidence will need to be provided.
- Sole carer of a parent/s or sole carer of a sibling if not living at home. Evidence needed from your school
- Refugee status. Evidence needed from the Home Office
- Non-selective state school that you attend has a lower than national average percentage of pupils achieving more than 5 GCSEs at grade A*-C. Will be looked at in reference to Department for Education performance tables.

If applicants meet both criteria from group A, then you will be emailed by admissions to send in evidence for group B after 15th October.

Entrance Exam

UKCAT (first cohort will be 2017 entry)

A Levels

BBB to include chemistry and biology/human biology. Same criteria for other A levels as listed under A100 programme.

Leicester Medical School

International Baccalaureate

Minimum 32 points-three Higher level subjects to include biology and chemistry and three Standard level subjects. Minimum 5 points in each subject.

GCSEs

Minimum grade C in english language, maths and two sciences (to include chemistry) or double science

BTEC

DDD in applied science or single BTEC with 2 A levels in chemistry and biology

Access Courses Accepted

Access to medicine or access to science applicants cannot apply for A199

Extra Application Information

- Resits for A levels: Module re-sits within the two years are accepted. Applicants resitting the whole of year 12 or 13, need to contact the university about significant mitigating circumstances, in order to be given permission to apply.
- UCAS reapplication: If you were successful on getting a conditional offer and then have to repeat A2 year because of serious mitigating circumstances, the university may allow you to apply again. In this situation, applicants are recommended to complete a degree and then apply as a graduate. The university will consider reapplications from students who were unsuccessful after interview, but need to show a significant improvement in their interview scores.
- Deferred entry: It is accepted for the A100 programme and needs to be stated in the UCAS application. It is not accepted for graduates.
- Medical school transfers: Not offered
- Internal transfers: Not offered

Admissions Data

Number of applications - A100: 2500, A199: new for 2017
Number of interview places - A100: 900 (40), A199: 96
Total number on course - A100: 241 (17), A199: 25

Applications
Non-academic Requirements

The university are looking for work experience that shows that you can communicate with the public.

Interview Selection

GCSE grades, A/AS levels (only look at confirmed grades), actual/predicted degree (graduates) and UKCAT result will be looked at and applicants will be given an overall score. Highest scoring applicants are invited for interview. Points given for GCSEs, A/AS levels and degrees can be found on the website. For the foundation programme, if you were unable to complete the 6-8 GCSEs required for scoring, you will need to ask your school to email, medfound@le.ac.uk before 15th October and this may then be taken into consideration. Access to medicine candidates will be ranked on academic UCAS form, UKCAT, references/employment and personal statement. Graduates on the access to medicine course will be scored for interview as a graduate.

Interview information

MMIs last for just over an hour. There will be 8 stations (manned and unmanned) based on the GMC document 'Tomorrow's Doctors.' Offers will be made based on performance at interview and the UCAS form may possibly be looked at in case of tie-breaks. Personal statements are not normally looked at, apart from to differentiate between 'borderline' applicants and tie-breaks.

Interview Season

December to February

Interview Outcome

Some offers will be made after each round of interviews, although most will be later in the year. You will hear from early January to mid-May.

Accommodation - Guarantee of Halls

Offer guaranteed accommodation to all first year students providing you submit your application before the deadline. Rooms are allocated on a first come, first serve basis with some priority given to students with specific requirements.

Student Perspective
Unique Selling Points

- A new curriculum started for the academic year 2016/17 which focuses on earlier patient contact, an emphasis on clinical relevance in the pre-clinical years and more time allocated for certain rotations such as GP

Leicester Medical School

- A brand new centre for Medicine opened in September 2015 which offers great facilities
- Free iPads are given to every medical student

Things to Consider
- You can only intercalate after your 3rd year, this limits your flexibility. if you wish to intercalate at another time it is a lengthy process to get permission.

- You learn multiple modules at the same time rather than focusing on one module at a time
- Accommodation is allocated on a first come, first served basis and so you need to be quick to get the accommodation you want

University of Liverpool - School of Medicine

Contact Details

School of Medicine, University of Liverpool, Cedar House, Ashton Street, Liverpool, L69 3GE

E: Mbchb@liv.ac.uk

T: 0151 795436

T: 0151 795 4370 (A100 and A101)

T: 0151 7949490 (789S)

Courses Offered:

A100

A101 (Graduate Entry)

789S (Foundation Programme)

Background

Liverpool University has been teaching medicine for nearly 200 years and there are about 1800 medical undergraduate students studying at the university at any one time. Alongside the medical school, there is the School of Tropical Medicine, School of Cancer Studies and world-leading life science research institutes.

Course Information

The course is taught through case based learning, small group teaching, workshops and lectures. It is based on a spiral curriculum. There are four horizontal themes that run through the course: psychology and sociology in medicine; population perspective; communication for clinical practise and therapeutics. There are five vertical themes that through the course: research and scholarship, patient safety, leadership and management, professionalism, the chronically ill patient, the acutely ill patient and the science of medicine.

Anatomy

Dissection is not offered, but prosections are used along with anatomical models, images and computer assisted learning (CAL) programmes.

Intercalation

It is optional to intercalate after 4th year and students can do this externally.

University of Liverpool - School of Medicine

Elective

5 weeks at the end of 4th year

Entry Requirements - A100

Entrance Exam

UKCAT (schools leavers): 2017 = 1930, 2016 = 2500

GAMSAT (graduates): Threshold for the past three years has been overall 55 with no less than 50 in any sections.

A Levels

AAA to include biology, chemistry and a third academic subject. General studies is not considered as one of the 3 A levels.

International Baccalaureate

36 points to include biology, chemistry and one other subject at Higher level; minimum 6 points in each. Three subjects at Standard level with minimum 5 points in each.

Scottish Highers

AAAAB-AAAAA with biology and chemistry at grade A at Advanced Higher.

Welsh Baccalaureate

Not acceptable as third A level

GCSEs

Nine in different subject areas to include core and additional science or triple science (biology, chemistry and physics), english language and mathematics all at grade B. A total of at least 15 points from the nine different subjects (A*/A=2, B=1...). Two points is the maximum for each subject area; only two in total for both maths and further maths, only two for dual award subjects, dual science up to four points. Short course GCSEs will at most get half the points of a full GCSE; two short courses can used instead of a full GCSE.

Graduates

Upper 2:1 in a biology, biomedical or health science degree OR another subject provided that the applicant also has minimum As in biology and chemistry at A level (if taken after initial A levels, first A levels must be minimum BBB(B)) .

A Levels

Minimum 3 B's (plus B at AS level) to include biology and

chemistry. The AS level can be critical thinking or general studies.

International Baccalaureate

32 points with minimum 5 in chemistry and biology at Higher level. No subject should have less than 3 points awarded.

Access Courses Accepted

A900 pre-medical studies at Lancaster University (will not accept applications from this course if have resat A2 examinations)

Entry Requirements - A101

Entrance Exam

GAMSAT: Threshold for the past three years has been overall 55 with no less than 50 in any of the sections

Degree

Minimum good 2:1 degree in a biomedical or health science subject

A Levels

BBB to include chemistry and biology with fourth AS level at grade B. Passes are required in the practical elements. Further maths is not accepted as an A/AS level when maths A level is also taken.

International Baccalaureate

32 points to include 3 Higher level subjects to include biology and chemistry, which must be at least 5

Scottish Highers

AAAAA - AABBB in Highers plus AB in Advanced Highers. You must have achieved AS in biology and chemistry

Welsh Baccalaureate

Accepted with BBB in A levels in biology, chemistry and another academic subject

GCSEs

Minimum grade C in english and maths

Entry requirements - 789S Health and Veterinary Sciences (Medicine) Year 0 Foundation

Applicants study at Birkenhead or Carmel College, St Helens in year 0

University of Liverpool - School of Medicine

Elibility

The course is targeted for applicants with substantial work place experience, related vocational qualifications instead of A levels, mature students or students who have taken a break from studies. Will not accept students who have completed A levels or school leavers.

Entrance Exam

No entrance exam is required and this includes when you are transferring onto the A100 programme

GCSEs

5 subjects at minimum grade B to include english language, maths and a science subjects

Graduates

Non-science graduates who achieved a 2:1 will be looked at if they graduated more than 5 years ago

Extra Application Information

- Resits for A levels: Need to be taken in one sitting usually after two years of study. If taken over three years, applicants should talk about extenuating circumstances and reasons why they did not achieve the grades in the first sitting in their personal statement. Any offer made is likely to be higher such as A* to reflect the longer study.
- UCAS reapplication: Only one further consecutive application is accepted for the same programme after rejection from a previous UCAS application. Personal statement should not be identical and show the potential that has been gained between applications. Applicants who have applied for the Foundation programme (789S) and been rejected after interview will not be considered again.
- Deferred entry: It is not possible for overseas students, year 0 entry and A101 (graduate entry). It is possible for the A100 programme.
- Medical school transfers: Not offered
- Internal transfers: Not offered

Admissions Data

Number of applications - A100: 1868 (23), A101: 357, 789S: 100

Number of interview places - A100: 962 (95), A101: 148, 789S: 20

Total number on course - A101: 278 (23), A101:29, 789S: 12

Applications

Non-academic Requirements

No formal work experience is required although demonstration and insight into a healthcare career will need to be shown.

Interview Selection

Application stages (A100 and A101)

Stage 1 (academic ability and admissions tests)
A level and GCSE grades (preference may be given to candidates with higher GCSE scores- non graduate applicants). For graduate applicants, degree classification will also be taken into account. UKCAT or GAMSAT mark-thresholds are determined each year. Any applicants with UKCAT Situational Judgement Test Band 4 will not progress further in the application process.

Stage 2 (non-academic criteria)
Applicants that demonstrate high academic potential in Stage 1 progress to stage 2. Criteria: demonstration and insight into a healthcare career will need to be shown; contribution to the community; critical, coherent and informative approach to communication; understanding of values that underpin good healthcare practise. Information from the academic reference is also considered.

Stage 3 (Interview)
Will be invited to interview if the applicant competitively met Stage 1 and Stage 2 requirements.

789S: If you meet the academic requirements along with relevant experience listed in your personal statement, you have a good chance of being selected for interview.

Interview Information

A100 and A101: MMIs will be based on values based recruitment and selecting for excellence report (see website for more detail). Overall scores are ranked and top-scoring applicants are made an offer.
789S: panel interview with two members of staff.

Interview Season

A100 and A101: February, 789S: March

Interview Outcome

After 31st March

University of Liverpool - School of Medicine

Accommodation - Guarantee of Halls

Guaranteed accommodation in first year if you put Liverpool as your first choice

Student Perspective

Unique Selling Points

- Opportunity to spend a Year in China at an english speaking university to study medicine and Chinese. This however extends the degree by an extra year.
- Finals take place at the end of 4th year, so you have 5th year to focus on clinical placements.

- Teaching is high quality with clinicians and academics holding at least a level one qualification as a clinical teacher.

Things to Consider

- Big cohort size so there are quite a lot of students on each clinical placement
- Elective is for a shorter time period
- Learning is very self-directed and so you need to be motivated and organised

University of Manchester - School of Medicine

Contact Details

Faculty of Biology, Medicine and Health, The University of Manchester, Oxford Road, Manchester, M13 9PL

E: ug.medicine@manchester.ac.uk

T: 0161 306 6000 / 0161 306 0211

Courses Offered

A106 (Undergraduate Five Year Course - same as A100) Option to apply for European Studies programme after being accepted onto A106

A104 (Foundation Programme)

Background

Medicine in Manchester started in 1814 with the opening of a school of anatomy. From 1824 multiple medical schools opened in Manchester which eventually ended up joining in 1836. Victoria University formed from Manchester Royal College of Medicine and Surgery with Owens College (life sciences) in 1800. Victoria University was one of the institutions that formed the new University of Manchester in 2004. Most recently in 2016 the Faculty of Biology, Medicine and Health was formed bringing together the department of Life Sciences (draws in international funding and offers a large number of courses from BSc to PhD) and the department of Medical and Human Sciences. The aim is to integrate biology, clinical application and patient care in one faculty to improve people's lives.

Course Information

The pre-clinical years are made up of laboratory sessions, anatomy teaching, weekly PBL sessions and approximately 5-6 hours of lectures. Each term is based around a body system with a spiral curriculum so the systems are revisited in clinical years. Clinical years still have PBLs and some lectures. There is the option to apply for the European Studies Program during your first term after being accepted onto the A106 programme. The languages available to study are French, German and Spanish. Students usually need to have the equivalent of an A level in the language. Students who choose this option essentially study medicine and a language. Students attend languages classes in the day during preclinical years and in the evening in clinical years. A104: The foun-

University of Manchester - School of Medicine

dation year is taught at the University of Manchester and Xaverian College.

Anatomy

Dissection is compulsory (although it is possible to be an observer only) and students work in groups of 8-10 students are are assigned to one cadaver. Anatomy teaching is supplemented with prosections.

Intercalation

Intercalation is offered and can be taken after the 2nd, 3rd or 4th year of the course. If the content of the intercalated degree differs sufficiently from the courses offered at Manchester, it is possible to intercalate externally.

Elective

Usually 8 weeks at the end of 4th year. Students on the A106 course with European studies get to spend 4 months in 5th year at one of the partner universities in Europe.

Entry Requirements - A106
Entrance Exam

UKCAT: 2017 = 1960, 2016 = 2660, 2015 = 2560

A Levels

AAA to include chemistry, plus one from the following subjects; biology or human biology, physics, mathematics or further mathematics. The third subject must be rigorous and therefore not include critical thinking, citizenship or general studies.

Three sciences are acceptable at A2 level unless you have biology and human biology or maths and further maths. Do not accept applied A-levels. Two AS levels in the place of one A2 level are not accepted. Normally expect four subjects at AS level excluding general studies. If due to policies at the school this is not possible, applicants will not be disadvantaged if written confirmation of the policy is provided by the school.

Unit grade information will form part of the consideration of applicants, they will not form part of offer conditions except for mathematics programmes.

If an applicant has already achieved A levels grades (AAA to include chemistry), the applicant will be considered even if their GCSEs do not match the required standard. However, the GCSEs must still have a minimum grade B in english language and mathematics. The sciences must be at minimum grade C at GCSE or AS or dual award science at BB.

International Baccalaureate

37 points overall. At least 766 at Higher levels including chemistry and 555 at Standard levels. Higher level subjects include chemistry, plus biology, physics or mathematics plus one further academic subject. Any sciences not taken at Higher level must be taken at Standard level or at GCSE. Alternatively a referee's statement confirming proficiency at Intermediate level in one unexamined science subject is deemed acceptable. If maths and English language are not offered they should have a minimum grade B at GCSE or IGCSE. The english language course taken in the IB must be clarified with the medicine admissions office before sending in the application.

Scottish Highers

AAAAB (awarded in the same sitting in one attempt). English language and any science subject (maths, physics, chemistry or biology) not taken at Higher/ Advanced Higher must have been achieved at SCQF level 5. Require Scottish Advanced Highers in addition to Scottish Highers.

Welsh Baccalaureate

Pass the Welsh Baccalaureate Advanced Diploma including two science A levels at AA to include chemistry

GCSEs

At least seven subjects at grade C or above. At least five GCSEs need to be at a grade A or A* (excluded are applied ICT, applied business, applied maths, short courses and BTEC qualifications). English language and maths have to be at a minimum grade B. Physics and biology are required at AS or GCSE at grade C or above (chemistry is required at A2 level). If dual award science or core and additional science, the minimum is BB. For 2017 entry due to the introduction of GCSE reform, the university will accept a mixture of GCSEs.

Graduates

Achieved or predicted a 2:1 degree. Minimum BBB in A levels to include chemistry, a second science plus one other academic subject on the first attempt (do not accept A2 re-sits). GCSE maths and english language at minimum grade B.

University of Manchester - School of Medicine

Access Courses Accepted

Only accept applicants with one of the following access to medicine courses:

- College of West Anglis, King's Lynn: Access to Medicine and Dentistry
- The Manchester College: Access to Medicine
- Sussex Downs College, Lewes: Access to Medicine
- Stafford College and New College,Telford: Access to Higher Education (Medicine and Health Professionals)

Entry Requirements - A104

Entrance Exam

UKCAT: 2017 = 1800, 2016 = 2510, 2015 = 2450

A Levels

AAA. If applicants have been given an offer and have done exceptionally well at interview but fail to reach the grades, they may still be accepted. A level grades must be achieved in one sitting within two years. The combinations of A levels accepted are: 3 rigorous arts/humanities subjects; 2 rigorous arts/humanities subjects and 1 science subject or 1 rigorous arts/humanities subject and 2 sciences subjects (not including chemistry). Critical thinking, general studies and applied A levels are not accepted. Any applicant studying chemistry and one other science or studying maths, physics and biology at A level will not be eligible to apply for A104.

International Baccalaureate

Same combination of Higher level subjects as listed under A levels. 35 points overall to include 666 at Higher level and 555 at Standard level.

Scottish Highers

AAA in Advanced Highers - combination of subjects accepted are the same as listed under A levels for A104. AAAAB in Highers. English language and any science subject not taken at Advanced/ Higher level must be taken at SCQF level 5.

Welsh Baccalaureate

Pass to include AA in two A levels. The A levels can not be in chemistry and another science.

GCSEs

At least six GCSEs at minimum grade C with at least four of them at A or A* level (these do not have to be in scienc-es but applied ICT and business, short courses and BTEC qualifications are not accepted). Biology, chemistry and physics need to at minimum grade C if not taken at AS/A level. Dual award science or core with additional science are accepted if a minimum of BB is achieved. English language and maths are required at minimum grade B. If you are applying with known grades of AAA at A level taken in one sitting within two years then the GCSE standards do not need to be achieved with the exceptions of the grades listed for maths, english language and sciences listed above.

Extra Application Information

- Resits for A levels: A level exams should be taken at the same sitting within two years. Re-sit applications are only considered with extenuating circumstances and AAB would have to be achieved in the first attempt to include chemistry and a second science. Reference to re-sits must be included in their personal statement and evidence of extenuating circumstances provided by school/college. It is normally required that A* AA will be obtained after the re-sit with A* achieved in the subject that was taken again.
- UCAS reapplication: If rejected before interview previously, contact the admissions office before completing the UCAS form. The admissions team normally re-consider applicants who were rejected after interview. A difference needs to be seen in your application from the previous year. If offered a place and declined or failed to make the non-academic conditions, you will be unable to apply again.
- Deferred entry: Deferred entry is accepted; the university encourages students to use the time in an imaginative way.
- Medical school transfers: Not offered
- Internal transfers: Not offered

Admissions Data

Number of applications - A106: 2200, A104: 220
Number of interview places - A106 & A104 combined: 1000
Total number on course - A106: 372 (28), A104: 20 (0)

Applications

Non-academic Requirements

There is a requirement to have voluntary caring work experience. Clinical work experience in the hospital or at

University of Manchester - School of Medicine

the GP is not essential and does not replace the voluntary caring work experience. Each applicant must complete an online information form in regards to non-academic activities. Applications without this form will be rejected.

Interview Selection

Pre-interview screening process looks at academic grading, personal statements, reference and UKCAT ranking. It is the same process for both A104 and A106 applicants, although the threshold used for UKCAT for A106 is likely to be lower. From 2017, the university will mostly look at the non-academic information form and will only read a few personal statements. Areas looked at on the personal statement/non-academic information form can be found on the website.

Interview information

MMI to include seven stations, with each station lasting seven minutes. There is a two- minute gap between each station to prepare for the next station.

Interview Season

January, for students who cannot make the January dates there will be 3 allocated half days in February and March

Interview Outcome

End of March

Accommodation - Guarantee of Halls

An offer of residence in halls is guaranteed to all UK/EU undergraduates in their first year of study if they are studying for their first degree.

Student Perspective
Unique Selling Points

- There is the option to study a European language alongside your medical course and you will get awarded with MBChB with European Studies at the end of the degree. It gives you the chance to spend 16 weeks in that country on elective.
- Communication teaching is a particular strength on the course.
- There are additional study opportunities on offer such as the Manchester Leadership Programme and language courses via the LEAP programme (there may be additional costs).

Things to Consider

- There is a chance you may spend your clinical years in Preston. if you are allocated this as your base hospital, most students have to move there.
- The learning style is very much student lead which is great for independent learners but won't suit everyone.
- Travel distances to clinical placements can be long. Some students have had to travel to the Isle of Man!

Newcastle University Medical School

Contact Details

Faculty of Medical Sciences, The Medical School, Framlington Place, Newcastle University, Newcastle Upon Tyne, NE2 4HH

E: sme@ncl.ac.uk

T: 01912085020

Courses Offered

A100

A100 (Widening Participation - PARTNERS Programme)

A101 (Graduate Entry)

Background

Medicine has been taught at Newcastle since 1834, it was actually the founding department of the university. There is a longstanding relationship with the University of Durham; a joint established organisation was formed in 1970 called The Durham University College of Medicine-Newcastle upon Tyne. The University of Newcastle upon Tyne was actually established in 1963. A high number of graduates from the course choose to work in the region after. The university in 2011 built a medical campus in Malaysia (not open to UK/EU applicants) and prides itself on taking an international approach.

Course Information

The course is based on a spiral curriculum and is taught through a focus on case based scenarios along with small group seminars, clinical skills sessions and lectures.

Anatomy

Taught using prosections, dissection is not offered.

Intercalation

Optional, most students intercalate after 3rd year. Students can intercalate at another university provided that the programme is deemed acceptable by a senior tutor.

Elective

8 weeks at the end of 4th year.

Entry Requirements - A100
Entrance Exam

UKCAT: 2016 = 2730, 2015 = 2300, 2014 = 2980

Newcastle University Medical School

A Levels

AAA to include chemistry and/or biology at A/AS level. General studies and critical thinking are not accepted. Biology, chemistry and physics A levels require a pass in the practicals. If only one of biology or chemistry is offered at A/AS level, the other subject should be offered at GCSE grade A (this can include Dual Award Science at this level).

International Baccalaureate

38 points or above. All subjects need grade 5 or above with Higher Level grade 6 in chemistry or biology. Two sciences, mathematics and english are desirable.

Scottish Highers

AAAAA at Higher grade to include chemistry and/or biology. If only one of chemistry or biology is at Higher level, then the other subject should have been taken at National 5 with grade A (alternatively grade 1 Standard grade or Intermediate 2 equivalent). Note they accept Scottish Highers in more than one sitting.

Welsh Baccalaureate

Grade A in Diploma with two A levels at grade A in chemistry and biology

GCSEs

Biology or chemistry at grade A if not offered at AS or A level

Graduates

Achieved or expected to achieve an honours degree in any discipline with an upper 2:1, first class honours or Integrated Master's Degree.

Access Courses Accepted

Access to Higher Education Diploma (medicine). Contact the medical school for the courses accepted.

PARTNERS Programme (Widening Participation)

- Must meet at least one of the nine eligibility criteria:
- Attended one of the listed sixth form schools or colleges on the website
- Attended one of the listed GCSE schools on the website
- Home postcode check on the website
- Entitled to free schools meals, school payments due to financial hardship or pupil premium funding
- Been in local authority care
- Neither parents have attended university and the main earner in the household does not have a professional occupation (check on the website)
- Disability or a long-term health condition and receive Personal Independence Payment (PIP)
- If you are a carer
- If you live independently from your parents due to estrangement.

You must also meet all of the following requirements: live in England, have home student fee status, have not already attended university, have not left more than one year ago from school/college.

A levels: ABB to include chemistry and/ or biology at AS or A level. Do not accept general studies or critical thinking. Biology, chemistry and physics require a pass in the practicals. If only one or biology and/or chemistry is offered at A or AS level, the other subject must be offered at GCSE grade B (dual award science grade B).

Entry Requirements - A101
Entrance Exam

UKCAT: 2016 = 2880, 2015 = 2910, 2014 = 3070

Degree

Upper 2:1 degree or integrated Master's degree or be a practising health care professional (post-registration qualification). Applicant must have sustained academic endeavour within the past three years.

Other Qualifications

Masters qualifications, A levels and GCSEs will not be incorporated into deciding whether the applicant will be interviewed or offered a place.

Extra Application Information

- Resits for A levels: Grades should be achieved on the first attempt. Resits may be considered: extenuating circumstances must be provided with evidence from your school or GP.
- UCAS reapplication: Can reapply with no limit to number of applications
- Deferred entry: Will consider applications for one year provided they show a plan to use the time well.

Newcastle University Medical School

Once offers have come through, deferrals will not usually be accepted.

- Medical school transfers: Not offered
- Internal transfers: Newcastle BSc students registered on a programme in the School of Biomedical Sciences, Faculty of Medical Sciences may apply for the A100 programme in their 1st year (up to 7 places). Students must achieve an average of 75% in year 1,in each module score at least 65% and complete the UKCAT.

Admissions Data

Number of applications - A100: 1293 - 2934, A101: 823 - 1213
Number of interview places - A100: 1000, A101: 600
Total number on course - A100: 318 (26), A101: 25

Applications

Non-academic Requirements

Applicants need to be able to show a commitment to caring such as volunteering at a hospice, care home, nursery or helping someone less fortunate.

Interview Selection

Applicants that fulfil the academic requirements on their first attempt as well as studying within the past 3 years (excludes CPD courses) proceed to the next stage. In extreme situations, the university may consider extenuating circumstance when the student did not attain grades on their first attempt. Applicants are then selected for interview based on their UKCAT score: the threshold is set each year depending on the competition.

Interview information

All interviews will be in the form of MMIs, which include role-play, interview questions and task driven exercises. Grades will be given for each station and this will determine offers (interviewers will have access to the applicant's personal statement and reference before and during an interview).

Interview Season

Mid November - early March

Interview Outcome

March

Accommodation - Guarantee of Halls

First years are guaranteed a place in University accommodation providing you accept Newcastle as your firm choice and complete the application on time. Note the guarantee may include that you share a room at the start of term. Mature undergraduate students (over 25) are allowed to choose accommodation within both undergraduate and postgraduate options.

Student Perspective
Unique Selling Points

- There are 3 SSC periods in 4th year where you are allowed to choose 6 week placements in your area of choice, this offers more flexibility to spend time in the specialities you are interested in.
- It is fun student city to live in with great nightlife and the rent is really cheap.
- The university offers brilliants schemes to increase access into medicine: Partners Programme and internal transfer from other science courses.

Things to Consider

- There can be limited specimens to look at in anatomy and with a lot of students this can make it difficult to get adequate time to learn from them.
- The electives and SSC placements in 4th year run from January to August and can make some students feel unprepared going into 5th year, as they have been out of formal teaching for a while.
- Placements can be outside of Newcastle and if placed in Teeside, students are advised to relocate there for the academic year. During the interview, you will be asked about your willingness to relocate.

Norwich Medical School (UEA)

Contact Details
University of East Anglia, Norwich Research Park, Norwich, NR4 7TJ
med.ug.admiss@uea.ac.uk
01603591515 / 01603456161

Courses Offered
A100
A104 (Foundation Programme)

Background
The medical school is part of the Faculty of Medicine and Health Sciences which includes other courses such as physiotherapy, midwifery, nursing, occupational therapy and speech and language therapy. The school is a partner of Norwich Research Park and is situated extremely close by. The research park is one of Europe's leading centres for food and health research and also hosts Norfolk and Norwich University Hospital.

Course Information
The course style is heavily focused towards small group teaching both at the university and at hospitals with about 10 students in a group. The course is taught through the body systems and PBLs feature strongly on the timetable. There are also lectures and large group seminars with 60 students.

Anatomy
Dissection is compulsory and occurs in years 1-3. Prosection is also used to teach anatomy. On top of this there is also the option to choose anatomy as a SSC.

Intercalation
Intercalation is optional after year 3 or 4 and at the moment the university offers only Masters. Intercalation can be taken externally.

Elective
4 weeks at the end of year 4

Entry requirements - A100
Entrance Exam
UKCAT: Do not have a cut off value for UKCAT. It is unusual

Norwich Medical School (UEA)

for an applicant with a score lower than the third decile to be invited to interview, this was 2400 in 2015. SJT banding is not currently used for the selection process.

A Levels
AAA to include biology/human biology and either physics or chemistry. Sciences must have a pass in the practicals. There is no pre-requisite for the third A level in terms of subject choice. Only one of mathematics and further mathematics at A level or AS level will be considered.

International Baccalaureate
36 points with 666 at Higher level to include biology and either chemistry or physics

Scottish Highers
AAA to include biology and either physics or chemistry. A minimum of grade B in a fourth Standard Highers subject.

Welsh Baccalaureate
Accepted as a fourth subject alongside 3 A levels (one biology, one other science subject and any other subject)

GCSEs
Minimum of six GCSEs at grade A or above to include English, maths and two science subjects. Short course GCSEs are not accepted. The university usually looks at the best 9 results to include the subjects listed above, they will only include one maths, up to two english and up to three single science subjects or a double science award. Repeat GCSEs are accepted.

Graduates
Minimum 2:1 classification in your degree. Need to show you have studied within the past three years. Minimum ABB in A levels to include biology/ human biology and one other science subject from chemistry or physics. If they were not taken in the original sitting, they need to be taken and a minimum A achieved. If applicants repeated A level study prior to university, their application will not be considered. The applicant must meet the requirements for GCSE and UKCAT.

Access Courses Accepted
The College of West Anglia (Access to Medicine)
Lambeth College (Access to Medicine & Biomedical Science)
Lancaster University (Pre-Medical Studies)
City and Islington College (Access to Medicine & Medical Bio Sciences)
The Manchester College (Access to Medicine)
Bradford University (Foundation in Clinical Science/Medicine)
Sussex Downs University (Access to Medicine)
City of Liverpool University (Access to Science)

Applicants must also meet the GCSE and UKCAT requirements. If the applicant holds A levels, they must have got a minimum ABB at first sitting irrespective of subjects. If the applicant holds a degree, this must be a minimum 2:1 classification.

Entry requirements - A104
Eligibility
In year 13 or have not been out of education for more than 3 years after finishing A levels and starting the A104 programme. Compulsory criterion: the secondary school you attend must have 60% or less students gaining more than 5 A*-C GCSES including maths and english in the year you achieved your GCSEs. Look on the website: www.education.gov.uk/schools/performance/. Applicants must also meet another of the criteria listed: household income less than £35,000 not including government benefits, been in local authority care or currently live in East Anglia. Applicants who live in East Anglia and those whose parents did not go on and study at higher education will be given particular consideration.

Entrance Exam
UKCAT

A Levels
BBB in A levels over two years. Any science A levels must include a pass in the practicals. Critical thinking and general studies are not accepted.

International Baccalaureate
32 points

GCSEs
Minimum six GCSEs at grade B to include english language, maths and a single science subject/BB in double award science.

Norwich Medical School (UEA)

Extra Application Information

- Resits for A levels: If applicants are taking their A levels over more than two years, certain rules apply to the grades. If they are re-sitting one subject they are required to get an A* in that subject, re-sitting two A level subjects they are required to get A*A and re-sitting three A level subjects they are required to get A*AA. Note - any subject that is being taken again, the grade awarded needs to be at least one grade higher than what was originally achieved.
- UCAS reapplication: Applications will only be considered for two consecutive years. Only one application is permitted for the foundation year programme.
- Deferred entry: Deferred entry is accepted but it is needs to be declared from the beginning on a UCAS application. There is no guarantee that a request made later on will be accepted.
- Medical school transfers: Not offered
- Internal transfers: Not offered

Admissions Data

Number of applications - A100: 1400, A104: 200
Number of interview places - A100: 600, A104: 94
Total number on course - A100: 167 (13), A104: 25

Applications
Non-academic Requirements

Applicants will be expected to draw on personal experience at interview to demonstrate understanding, suitability and insight into becoming a doctor. You will be expected to print out and fill in the work experience form and bring it to the interview.

Interview Selection

A100 - Primary screening: check applicants meet the minimum academic entry criteria, have completed the UKCAT test in the same year as the application and have a satisfactory personal statement and references. Secondary screening: academic qualifications including UKCAT are assessed and ranked. The highest scores are invited to interview.

A104 - Primary screening: meet minimum academic entry requirements. Applicants asked to provide evidence for contextual criteria. Secondary screening: ranked using GCSEs, UKCAT and contextual criteria. References and personal statements will also be looked at. The highest scores are invited to interview.

Interview Information

MMIs last 50 minutes. There are 5 minutes for each of the 7 stations with 1.5 minutes in between the stations for changeover/preparation time.

A100: applicants are ranked based on the interview and UKCAT score. The top ranking applicants will receive offers.

A104: offers will be based on performance at interview and the rest of the application i.e. UKCAT, UCAS form, references etc.

Interview Season

A100: December to March
A104: late February to early March

Interview Outcome

Early to mid March

Accommodation - Guarantee of Halls

Guaranteed accommodation in your first year if you apply by the deadline and choose UEA as your firm choice. There are designated halls for medical and healthcare science students. Each flat will normally have half its residents from these courses (e.g. medicine, nursing, midwifery, physiotherapy).

Student Perspective
Unique Selling Points

- Extensive anatomy teaching and option to intercalate in a Masters in Medical Education and Research in clinical anatomy and surgery.
- Interdisciplinary approach with opportunities of group work with students from other healthcare degrees.
- Emphasis on small group work which makes you feel supported and means you get to know academics and other students better.

Things to Consider

- Elective abroad is only 4 weeks in year 4, although you get a home elective (you have to stay in the UK) of 6 weeks in year 5.
- Intercalation opportunities at the university are tailored towards doing a Masters and there are less options to choose from.
- It is a campus based university.

The University of Nottingham Medical School

Contact Details

Faculty of Medicine and Health Sciences, The University of Nottingham, Queen's Medical Centre, Nottingham, NG7 2UH

E: enquiries@nottingham.ac.uk

T: 0115 921 9924

T: 0115 9514749

Courses Offered

A100

A101 (Graduate Entry)

A108 (Foundation Programme)

Background

The medical school campus is part of the Queen's Medical Centre and opened in 1970; it is also used by other healthcare professionals such as midwifery, nursing and life science courses. The main campus called University Park is linked to the medical school via a pedestrian footbridge. A new campus was opened in Derby in 2003, which is used by graduate medical students and foundation medical students in their first year.

Course Information

The course is lecture based in the pre-clinical years and is taught by systems, for example for the cardiovascular system (CVS) module students learn about the anatomy, physiology, histology, basic pathology and pharmacology of that system. There are some problem-solving workshops and tutorials during the year but they are not the focus of teaching. There are 8-10 clinical sessions each pre-clinical year which are preceded by a clinical skills workshop so that you can practice the skills in the hospital or the GP. The graduate programme is PBL based for the first year and a half and then the graduates join the undergraduate course for the clinical phases.

Anatomy

Dissection of cadavers is a compulsory part of the timetable over two semesters in 1st and 2nd year in groups of 5

Intercalation

You are awarded a separate degree (BMedSci) already as it is integrated in the 5 year course. The BMedSci occurs

The University of Nottingham Medical School

in the first semester of third year and does not require an extra year of study (this is also why it scores less FPAS points). It can be done in almost any area of biomedical sciences and medicine. Occasionally students have been given permission to take a year out to study for a PhD or Masters degree in between finishing the BMedSci degree and continuing with the A100 programme.

Elective

7 weeks in 5th year

Entry Requirements - A100

Entrance Exam

UKCAT is scored as followed for each of the four components (maximum of 30 points):

301-400 = 4 points, 401-500 = 5 points, 501-600 = 6 points, 601-700 = 7 points, 701-800 = 8 points, 801-900 = 9 points. SJT is scored: band 4 = application will not be taken any further, band 3 = 1 point, band 2 = 2 points, band 1 = 3 points.

A Levels

AAA to include chemistry and biology and a third A level in any subject. It does not include critical thinking, general studies, citizenship studies and global perspectives. Pass is needed in practical elements in the sciences if assessed separately.

International Baccalaureate

Minimum is 36 points, with minimum of 666 at Higher level to include biology and chemistry.

Scottish Highers

A grade at Advanced Highers in biology and chemistry with AAAAB at Highers to include maths, english language and the sciences (with an A in biology and chemistry).

Welsh Baccalaureate

AAA to include biology and chemistry. Welsh baccalaureate core can be used in lieu of the third A grade.

GCSEs

AAAAAA (6 As) to include chemistry, physics and biology or double science. Grade B in physics will be accepted if the applicant achieved an A at AS level. Grade B or above in english and maths.

Graduates

2:1 in a science related degree. AAA at A level to include biology and chemistry.

Access Courses Accepted

No specific courses listed on the website (contact admissions).

Entry Requirements - A101

Entrance Exam

GAMSAT a higher cut off score is normally required if the applicant has a lower 2:1 degree

Minimum score of 55 in section 2 and section 1 or 3 and a minimum score of 50 in the remaining section.

GAMSAT Scores:

2017 = 56 with a 2:1 and 58 with a 2:2

2016 = 60 with a 2:1 and 65 with a 2:2

2015 = 61 with a 2:1 and 66 with a 2:2

Degree

Minimum 2:2. Masters or PhD will be accepted instead of an undergraduate degree.

Entry Requirements - A108

Eligibility

- Living in a disadvantaged area of the UK
- Meet one of the following criteria (evidence will need to be provided):
- Are or in the past have been looked after by the local authority
- Living in a household that receives means-tested benefit with a household income less than £35,000
- Sole carer of a parent/s or sibling (if living away from home)
- Refugee status

You will not be accepted for this course if your A levels meet the entry requirements for the A100 course or if you are a graduate.

Entrance Exam

UKCAT

A Levels

BBC achieved over two years to include minimum B grade in chemistry and biology. Pass is needed in practical elements in the sciences if assessed separately. The re-sit policy is the same listed for the A100 course.

The University of Nottingham Medical School

International Baccalaureate

28 points to include 5 in Higher level biology and chemistry

GCSEs

Five GCSEs at grade B to include english language, maths, biology, chemistry and physics (science triple or double award). Applied science is not accepted.

Extra Application Information:

- Resits for A levels: Accept up to one module re-sit for every A level subject within the two years. Re-sits are not accepted after the A level has been awarded. A levels must be achieved within two years.
- UCAS reapplication: If you were unsuccessful after interview, you will not be able to reapply.
- Deferred entry: Accepted, but you must state this on your UCAS application
- Medical school transfers: Not offered
- Internal transfers: Not offered

Admissions Data

Number of applications - A100: 2500, A101: 870-1044, A108: 350

Number of interview places - A100: 700, A101: 250-300 A108: 150

Total number on course - A100: 240 (25), A101: 94, A108: 25

Applications
Non-academic Requirements

A100 and A108: Expectation that applicants will have some medical or voluntary work experience. Students are recommended to keep a reflective diary in order to have preparation material for personal statement and interview. If unable to gain clinical work experience, applicants are expected to have spoken to their GP about a career in medicine and have experience in a caring setting eg. care home.

A101: You will need paid or voluntary work experience in a healthcare setting. Applicants who have spent time doing work experience regularly over several months will be looked at favourably. Applicants who have completed work experience recently i.e within the last 18 months will also be looked at more favourably.

If you get an interview, applicants will need to upload academic certificates/transcripts and confirmation of work experience placements onto the portal.

Interview Selection

A100 and A108: You need to get higher than SJT band 4 (section of the UKCAT test). UKCAT and GCSEs (highest 8 GCSEs scored) added together- top 50% go through to next stage. GCSEs: biology, chemistry, physics, maths, english language and best three other subjects scored OR double science, maths, english and best four other subjects scored. GCSEs, UKCAT, personal statement and reference scored together and the top scoring applicants go through to interview

A101: achieve the minimum section requirements as well getting higher than the cut-off score in GAMSAT will get the applicant an interview place.

Interview Information

MMIs consist of 8 stations which last about 1 hour.2 stations involve role play and 6 stations involve answering questions on the scenarios or follow instructions for the designated task.

Each station is scored and these are totalled. Offers are made on the performance during the interview. The UKCAT score is used if there are identical scores between students.

Interview Season

A100 and A108: December to April, A101: March to April

Interview Outcome

A100: by the end of March, A108: by the end of February, A101: aim to send outcome within two weeks of the last set of interviews

Accommodation - Guarantee of Halls:

University accommodation is guaranteed for first year students. A100 students are located at University Park Campus, Jubilee Campus or University houses. A101 and A108 students are located on the Derby campus.

Student Perspective
Unique Selling Points

- The university offers an exchange programme which lets students spend a semester in their 2nd year in Australia or Norway. Selection of students is based on academic achievement.
- Dissection is with demonstrators who are surgical trainees or anatomy specialists and so you learn a lot from them.

The University of Nottingham Medical School

- The campus university park is a beautiful landscaped area and this is where most of the university is located.

Things to Consider

- The BMedSci scores one point less in FPAS applications compared to an intercalated degree.
- Students on the A101 and A108 course are located in Derby for their first year and so you are not near to the main university campus where most things are happening.
- It is possible to get 3 degrees in 6 years, by studying a Masters or a PhD as well as the BMedSci and A100 degrees. However, this is not advertised and so you have to be proactive.

Oxford University Medical School

Contact Details

Medical Sciences Office, University of Oxford, Level 3, John Radcliffe Hospital, Oxford, OX3 9DU

E: admissions@medschool.ox.ac.uk (A100)

T: 01865 285783 (A100)

E: geadmin@medsci.ox.ac.uk (A101)

T: 01865 228975 (A101)

Courses Offered

A100

A101 (Graduate Entry)

Background

Oxford University is the oldest university in the English-speaking world and so brings with it a whole lot of history. It runs as a collegiate university. Medicine was added to the courses taught during the 20th and early 21st century when sciences were added to the humanistic teaching. The medical school places a specific emphasis on research with an incorporated BA in medical sciences in the third year for undergraduates. Many of the students on the graduate course progress to careers within academic medicine. The course is very distinct with three years in pre-clinical medicine and then three years in Oxford/ London for clinical medicine.

Course Information

The course is taught through lectures, workshops and small tutorials conducted in the students college. Modules in the pre-clinical years focus on themes such as physiology and pharmacology and biochemistry and medical genetics. The course tends to have a more academic focus.

Anatomy

The university no longer offers dissection, instead they offer prosection.

Intercalation

This is a compulsory extra year which enables students to be awarded a BA in medical sciences at Oxford. The first three years are counted as preclinical with the third year called the BA year (Final Honour School of Medical Sciences). This leads to an honours BA in medical scienc-

Oxford University Medical School

es in one of five areas: neuroscience; molecular medicine; cardiovascular, renal and respiratory biology; infection and immunity or cellular physiology and pharmacology.

Elective

10 weeks in Year 4 or 6 (final year for A101 and A100)

Entry Requirements - A100

Entrance Exam

BMAT: Weighting - section 1 = 40% , section 2 = 40% and section 3 = 20%

2017: mean adjusted BMAT score was 53%, shortlisted it was 63% and those offered places it was 64%.

A Levels

A*AA to include at least grade A in chemistry and at least one of biology, physics or mathematics. The A* does not have to be in any specific subject. Critical thinking and general studies are not included. Practical elements in the A levels should be passed.

International Baccalaureate

Score of 39. Higher Level scores of 766 to include chemistry and at least one from biology, physics and maths.

Scottish Highers

AA in Advanced Highers in one academic year to include chemistry and one from biology, physics or maths. AAAAA in Highers in one academic year.

Welsh Baccalaureate

Expected to have studied three subjects at A level as part of the qualification. Offers will be based on the A levels rather than the baccalaureate award.

GCSEs

No specific requirements for GCSEs.

Mean number of A*s for all applicants was 8.2, it was 10.3 for those short-listed and 10.5 for those who received offers.

Mean proportion of A* for all applicants was 0.76, 0.92 for those short-listed and 0.93 for applicants receiving offers.

Graduates

Award or prediction of a first class or high 2:1 degree. Results in A levels should be as above.

Access Courses Accepted

The medical school does not recommend any particular access courses. It is up to the student to show that the course you are studying is a suitable alternative to A levels and covers the same content asked for in the entry criteria. Contact university admissions for further advice and guidance.

Entry requirements - A101

Entrance Exam

BMAT: Unlikely to be invited to interview if your score falls below the top 40%.

Degree

2:1 or above. Degree needs to be in applied and experimental science to include bioscience, chemistry, engineering and experimental physics. There is a partial list of acceptable degrees on the website but is not completely exhaustive. If the degree is not in bioscience then applicants must have biology or dual award science at GCSE or equivalent.

A Levels

Two science A levels or equivalent to include chemistry (unless you have a chemistry degree).

Extra Application Information:

- Resits for A levels: The grades achieved should be taken in one academic year. If the applicant has already achieved grade A at A level in one or more of the subjects listed above, the offer will be looked at, but they will still be required to achieve A*AA in the same academic year.
- UCAS reapplication: Can reapply with no limit to number of applications.
- Deferred entry: Applications are considered for deferred entry.
- Medical school transfers: In the third year of the course, students can apply to stay at Oxford for the clinical years or transfer to a medical school in London (UCL, Imperial, King's College London, St George's London and Barts (Queen Mary London)). If students are unsuccessful in applying to a London medical school, they are still guaranteed a space in Oxford. They may apply to or be allocated a different college for clinical years.
- Internal transfers: Not offered

Oxford University Medical School

Admissions Data

Number of applications - A100: 1500, A101: 400

Number of interview places - A100: 425, A101: no specific quota

Total number on course - A100: 145, A101: 30 (14 international places across the two courses)

Applications

Non-academic Requirements

Work experience in hospitals is desirable, but the university understands it can be difficult to organise and so there is no requirement for it. Any voluntary work is beneficial such as volunteering at an old people's home, for a charity or St John's Ambulance.

Interview Selection

There is a suggested reading list and advice for writing a personal statement online which emphasises the inclusion of the selection criteria into your statement.

A100: ranking for interview is based on equal weighting of GCSE performance and BMAT results. GCSE performance is a combination of the number of A* grades and the proportion of A* grades of all GCSEs achieved (not including short courses). This is in the context of the school at which the GCSEs have been sat (using government data). The same number of applicants are short-listed every year and there is not cut off for the BMAT or GCSEs. One score can compensate for a slightly lower score in the other element. Any applicants who do not make the initial shortlist are reviewed so that individual circumstances (academic and non-academic) can be taken into account for not reaching their potential. Applicants below the cut off for the shortlist and any applicants worthy of further consideration are reviewed and forty additional applicants are added to the shortlist.

A101: you will also need to fill out an additional application form for the university which must be submitted by 15th October. The application form needs to have attached a statement explaining why you want to study medicine at Oxford, and why you think you are suited to medicine. You will also need to put down three references. Look on the website for which colleges you can apply to for graduate medicine. Shortlisting will be based on scores from BMAT along with information from other documents in the application.

Interview Information

You will be Invited to two colleges: your college of choice if possible or an allocated college if you made an open application and the second will be random. Certain colleges will look for different characteristics so make sure to research them carefully. The invitation letter will come from the college in which you will be spending your first night. You will spend the afternoon and the night at this college and then go the second college on the next morning. The interviews in each college will be conducted by at least two academics and one practising clinician. The number of interviews may vary, but this has no relation to whether your application has been successful.

Interview Season

Mid December

Interview Outcome

Your college of choice will write (letter or email) to inform you of the outcome and it will be scheduled to arrive on a specific date in early January.

Accommodation - Guarantee of Halls

Colleges are able to provide accommodation for all undergraduates during their first year of study and at least one other year. Many colleges can also provide accommodation for graduates. The Graduate Accommodation Office can help graduates to find accommodation on sites owned by the university.

Student Perspective

Unique Selling Points

- The collegiate system really adds to the experience and each college has its own history, traditions, runs its own societies and has a bar.
- There is the option to transfer to London universities for the clinical years.
- There is an emphasis on tutorials in your college, which really helps consolidate your learning.

Things to Consider

- In the pre-clinical years, there is little exposure to patients and learning the practical skills.
- It is compulsory for the A100 programme to do the intercalated year in medical sciences.
- The course is heavily essay based both during the term time and in exams.

Plymouth University Peninsula – School of Medicine

Contact Details

Plymouth University Peninsula Schools of Medicine and Dentistry, The John Bull Building, Tamar Science Park, Plymouth, PL6 8BU

E: meddent-admissions@plymouth.ac.uk

T: 01752600600 / 01752 437333

Courses Offered

A100

Background

Plymouth University founded its own medical and dental school and is the only modern university in the UK to have done this. The university is also the largest provider of healthcare education in the South East. There is a strong partnership between Plymouth University and the NHS in Devon and Cornwall (Derriford Hospital and Torbay Hospital).

Course Information

Students learn from a spiral-based curriculum with year 1 looking at the healthy body and year 2 looking at illness and disease in the same body systems. Teaching is focused on small group teaching with PBLs, workshops and tutorials.

Anatomy

Taught through 3D models and anatomage virtual dissection. Dissection and prosection is not offered.

Intercalation

It is offered after year 4, but it is only available to small number of students

Elective

8 weeks in 5th year

Entry Requirements - A100

Entrance Exam

UKCAT: A minimum standard is set each year and there are also required standards in each of the sub-tests, the thresholds for the past few years can be found on the website.

2016 = 2610, 2015 = 2400, 2014 = 2671

Plymouth University Peninsula - School of Medicine

GAMSAT (non-direct school leavers): If it's more than two years since completing A levels or equivalent or if you are a graduate, you will need to take the GAMSAT.

Applicants offering the following qualifications will need to take the GAMSAT:
- BTEC National Diploma in Applied Science
- Advanced Diploma in Society, Health and Development
- Access to HE Diploma (Science)

Cut-off overall score for the past three years has been a total of 65. A minimum is required in the three sections; this varies slightly year to year. For 2017 it was: section 1-55, section 2-62, and section 3-61

A Levels
A*AA or AAA to include chemistry and either biology or physics. General studies is not included. If biology is not taken at A level, it must be offered at AS level.

International Baccalaureate
36-38 points overall to include Higher level biology and chemistry at level 6

Scottish Highers
AAA to include chemistry and biology.

Welsh Baccalaureate
Pass overall plus grades A*A-AA in chemistry and biology.

GCSEs
7 GCSEs at grades A-C. They must include english language, maths and either GCSE biology and chemistry or GCSE single and additional science.

Graduates
For graduates, the university only takes into consideration your GAMSAT score, they do not look at your degree level, A levels or GCSEs.

Access Courses Accepted
No specific courses listed (contact admissions for advice)

Extra Application Information
- Resits for A levels: Resits are accepted providing on the first attempt AAB was achieved.
- UCAS reapplication: Can reapply with no limit to number of applications.
- Deferred entry: Accepted but this must be made apparent when you apply.
- Medical school transfers: Not offered
- Internal transfers: If students are enrolled on BSc Biomedical Science and are in their 1st year, they can express interest into transferring onto the A100 programme for the next academic year. Interest must be submitted to the Admissions and Student Support Team before 15th October. Maximum of 20 students will be invited to interview for the Dentistry and Medicine programmes with a maximum of 5 students being granted transfer across the A100 and BDS (dentistry) programmes. You must achieve the equivalent of a 1st (>70% average) in BSc Year 1 assessments. A levels: AAB to include biology and chemistry. IB: 35 with 6 in Higher level in biology and chemistry. Scottish Highers: AAB at Advanced level to include biology and chemistry.
- Graduate entry transfer: If Plymouth students are on track to achieve a 1st or have achieved it within the last two years they can apply through UCAS and do not need to sit the GAMSAT. Eligible Plymouth University degree courses; Human Biosciences, Biomedical Sciences, Healthcare Science (Life Sciences or Physiological Sciences) and Exercise, Nutrition & Health.

Admissions Data
Number of applications - A100: 869
Number of interview places - A100: 405
Total number on course - A100: 86 (6)

Applications
Non-academic Requirements
No specific work experience is required. Work experience will NOT be looked at for interview selection, at interview or selecting who to give offers to.

Interview Selection
Applicants are shortlisted for interview based on UKCAT or GAMSAT scores alongside academic information on the UCAS form.

Interview Information
You will need to complete a written questionnaire to show your commitment and motivation to study medi-

Plymouth University Peninsula - School of Medicine

cine at the interview. You will be given three contemporary ethical scenarios and you will need to select one for the interview. The interview lasts approximately 20 minutes and aims to explore the student's attitudes, way of thinking and their outlook. The panel includes clinicians, patients and the public. They expect applicants to demonstrate the values included in the NHS constitution.

Interview Season

Late November - December (Reserved February dates for those applicants who were unable to make the previous interview dates for specific reasons)

Interview Outcome

Before christmas, those with interviews in February will hear within 2 weeks

Accommodation - Guarantee of Halls:

Accommodation is guaranteed to all undergraduates who choose Plymouth as their first choice.

Student Perspective

Unique Selling Points

- The Life Sciences Resource Centre allows you to learn under experts in the technology that is used in the NHS for example MRIs, ultrasounds and CT scans.
- The Clinical Skills Resource Centre has patient simulators and is set up as a replica of wards and emergency rooms. This means you get to practise your clinical skills in a safe simulated environment.
- The cohort size is small and so you get to know everyone in your year really well.

Things to Consider

- Intercalation is quite late in the degree course, it is just before you go into 5th year.
- Anatomy is only taught through models and not by looking at human tissue.
- School leavers and non-direct school leavers have to do separate admissions tests for the same course.

Queen's University Belfast - School of Medicine

Contact Details

School of Medicine, Dentistry and Biomedical Sciences, Whitla Medical Building, 97 Lisburn Road, Belfast, BT9 7BL

E: admissions@qub.ac.uk

T: 02890 972215 / 028 9097 3838

Courses Offered

A100

Background

A medical school in Belfast opened in 1835, although the college could not award degrees so medical students had to sit their finals and graduate from the University of Glasgow or Edinburgh until 1849. Queen's College Belfast opened in 1849 and received its Charter as The Queen's University of Belfast in 1908. There is a specific University Health Science Campus with two teaching hospitals and several University research centres located close by.

Course Information

The university breaks down the teaching in pre-clinical years into body systems. The course is taught through lectures and seminars/tutorials, which can vary in size from 8 to 40 students, practical classes and communication and clinical e-resources.

Anatomy

Dissection is compulsory and sessions are nearly every week

Intercalation

It is optional and students can intercalate at the end of 2nd or 3rd year

Elective

6 weeks at the beginning of 5th year.

Entry Requirements - A100
Entrance Exam

UKCAT: The overall score will be used and applicants can gain a maximum of 6 points. The points awarded for 2017 entry: >2200 = 6 points, 2040-2190 = 5 points, 1880-2030 = 4 points, 1720-1870 = 3 points, 1560-1710 = 2 points, 1400-1550 = 1 point, <1390 = 0 points

Queen's University Belfast - School of Medicine

The Situational Judgement Test was not used for 2017 entry but used for borderline applicants who have a similar score at interview.

A Levels

AAA (plus A in fourth AS level) to include chemistry and at least one from biology, human biology, physics and maths. Only one VCE/Applied subject at either A level or AS level (not both) is counted. If biology/human biology was not taken at A level it is required as an AS level; a grade A as the 4th AS level or grade B as the 5th AS level. Mathematics and further mathematics cannot be counted as two separate A levels but can be counted as one A Level and one AS level. General Studies and critical thinking is not accepted at AS or A level. The fourth AS level can be replaced by a grade A in the EPQ or Welsh Baccalaureate Advanced Diploma or a grade B in a 4th A level.

International Baccalaureate

Minimum 36 points, with 6 in chemistry and biology at Higher level

Scottish Highers

AAABB Highers (first attempt): 34 points for AAABB, 35 points for AAAAB, 36 points for AAAAA

Advanced Highers - the standard required ranges from AA to AAA. The AAA is required for those with AAABB in Highers and only AA for those with AAAAA in their Highers (all other applicants require three Advanced Highers). It must include chemistry (A) plus one from physics, biology and maths. Biology higher is the minimum requirement and physics and maths need to have been taken to at least Standard grade Intermediate 2 or National 5.

Welsh Baccalaureate

Advanced Welsh baccalaureate is accepted in lieu of 4th AS level

GCSEs

English, mathematics and physics (or Double Award Science) are needed at GCSE if not offered as AS or A levels. GCSEs will be scored to assess whether the candidate will be offered an interview. A total points score will come from the best 9 GCSEs on the first attempt (an exception if the GCSE was taken a year early and then repeated at the normal time). The points system gives an A* four points, and an A three points. GCSE Short Courses are given half the points for the same grade. Two short courses can be the equivalent as one GCSE. Additional grade A's at GCSE and year 13 academic AS achievement may be used to distinguish applicants who have the same points.

Applicants who have attended secondary schools in Northern Ireland will be assessed on AS level grades rather than GCSE performance as well as UKCAT and predicted A level grades.

Graduates

High 2:1 in degree with either:
ABB at A level
A2 B2 B2 B2 B2 B2 B2 at Higher level in the leaving certificate
ABBBB in Scottish Highers on first attempt
1:1 in degree or PhD with either:
BBB at A level or equivalent.
Science background: Chemistry and one other science at A level (grade C is the lowest grade that is accepted in either biology or chemistry at A level/AS level); biology taken to at least AS level; physics (or double science) and maths must be taken to at least GCSE.
Non-science background: Applicants are still required to achieve the grades listed above for A level on the first attempt and degree grading. Will be considered if the applicant takes the appropriate science exam on finishing their degree (contact admissions for guidance).

Access Courses Accepted

No specific access courses currently listed on the website (contact admissions for advice)

Extra Application Information

- Resits for A levels: Module repeats within the two years do not place applicants at a disadvantage. An A level taken a year early is accepted. Only applicants re-sitting their A levels that held a previous firm offer at Queen's (if made) will be accepted. They must have achieved AAB (plus A in AS level) on their first attempt.
- UCAS reapplication: Will only be able to apply to Queens for a second time if you put Queen's down for your first UCAS cycle as it shows commitment to the university from the start. This applies to applicants who get the grades needed in their first sitting

Queen's University Belfast - School of Medicine

and for those applicants who held an offer (if made) as a conditional firm but did not get the grades and are re-sitting (must have also achieved AAB plus A in a fourth AS level). Maximum of three cycles to medicine through UCAS, with a maximum of two attempts at A level or graduate stage.

- Deferred entry: May be accepted if you include it on your application.
- Medical school transfers: Not offered
- Internal transfers: Not offered

Admissions Data

Number of applications - A100: 1172
Number of interview places - A100: 700
Total number on course - A100: 252 (26)

Applications
Non-academic Requirements

Clinical work experience is not a specific requirement. It is encouraged that applicants have obtained caring experience. Students are expected to show evidence of commitment and motivation to include what the applicant has done to find out about medicine as a career choice e.g. clinical setting, medical careers conferences, voluntary work in a care setting.

Interview Selection

Previous academic performance is assessed including school and university grades if completed and UKCAT. Applicants are then ranked and scored and this allows applicants to be selected for interview.

Interview Information

MMI with 9 stations to evaluate non-cognitive skills; empathy, problem-solving, communication skills and ethical reasoning.

Offer will be made solely on interview performance.

Interview Season

Mid January and mid March

Interview Outcome

Early April

Accommodation - Guarantee of Halls

Students applying from outside of Northern Ireland are guaranteed accommodation whereas students from Northern Ireland are NOT guaranteed accommodation.

Student Perspective
Unique Selling Points

- There is the opportunity for students to take a clinical module in Europe as part of the ERAMUS programme
- Belfast is a cheap city to live in and boasts a great selection of entertainment
- There is the option to choose when to take your intercalated year, which gives you more flexibility

Things to Consider

- Clinical placements can be anywhere in Northern Ireland and so can be quite a distance to get to
- Students living in Northern Ireland do NOT have a guarantee of accommodation
- The university is still looking for a 4th AS level which some schools may not be offering (there are some qualifications they will look at in exchange for the 4th AS level)

Sheffield Medical School

Contact Details

The Medical School, The University of Sheffield, Beech Hill Road, Sheffield, S10 2RX, UK

E: medadmissions@sheffield.ac.uk

T: 0114 222 5531

Courses Offered

A100

Background

Sheffield medical school was founded in 1828, but the school has been recently refurbished to suit students of the 21st century and there is a brand new health science library. The medical school has a longstanding history of providing their students with good education, with engaged educators and plenty of research exposure.

Course Information

A broad and systems-based, integrated basic and clinical science curriculum teaching personal and professional skills and cultivating curiosity. Teaching is delivered from the perspective of the patient. The course is lecture-based and Problem based learning activities are incorporated into year 1 only.

Anatomy

Cadaver dissection and prosection

Intercalation

Offered after year 3 and can intercalate externally

Elective

7-8 weeks, in year 4

Entry requirements - A100

Entrance Exam

UKCAT: The minimum cut-off score for UKCAT is now 2460 for consideration for interview. The SJT is only considered with the MMI score.

2017 offer threshold = 2000/2700

2016 offer threshold = 2510/3600

2015 offer threshold = 2500/3600

Sheffield Medical School

A Levels

AAA, including chemistry and one of maths, physics, biology or psychology. Exceptions: Critical thinking and general studies

International Baccalaureate

36 points required overall with 6, 6, 6 at Higher level, including chemistry and another science. Also, at least 4's must be attained at Standard level.

Scottish Highers

AAAAB and Advanced Highers of AA including chemistry and another science

Welsh Baccalaureate

AA at A level, in chemistry and another science and grade A in the baccalaureate

GCSEs

At least 8x A*-C and at least 6 A grades in one sitting. grade C english language required.

Access Courses Accepted

Sheffield has a widening access to medicine programme called Sheffield Outreach and Access to Medicine Scheme (SOAMS), which is only open to students from a lower socioeconomic background and who have faced significant adversity which has prohibited them from attaining the grades normally expected of a medicine applicant due to family or schooling.

The following grade requirements are needed for students applying under this scheme:

A Levels

Provided SOAMS applicants complete the programme, they will be given an adjusted offer of AAB.

GCSEs

8 x grades C's at GCSE, including english, sciences and maths, and 6 x A*-B grades, in one sitting

UKCAT

Threshold is the same as for A100 at 2460/3600.

There is also The Realising Opportunities Scheme for which the entry requirements are the same as for A100 entry except the A level requirement is lowered to AAB.

Graduates

Graduates can apply for the 5 year programme provided they have a 2:1 or first class degree.

A Levels

Applicants must also have attained grades BBB in chemistry, although this can be taken pre or post degree and a predicted grade B will be accepted.
Entry Requirements - A104 (Foundation)
Please note the A104 foundation year has now been withdrawn from Sheffield from 2018.

Extra Application Information

- Resits for A levels: A levels must be sat within the two year window. Modular resits must be justified.
- UCAS reapplication: Can reapply with no limit to number of applications.
- Deferred entry: Can defer entry but must state in your personal statement your reasoning.
- Medical school transfers: Not offered
- Internal transfers: Not offered

Admissions Data

Number of applications - A100: 2000
Number of interview places - A100: 900
Total number on course - A100: 237 (18)

Applications
Non-academic Requirements

Personal statements are not given a score but instead are used for discussion at interview. Work experience is required and applicants should offer a variety of experiences.

Interview Selection

Applicants are screened based on their academic results and UKCAT. Then applicants are ranked according to the 'Roles and Responsibilities' form regarding work experience undertaken and their reference is also considered; widening participation is an important consideration in Sheffield applications.

Interview Information

Multiple mini interviews format, usually with 2 clinical academics and a lay member. You should be familiar with the NHS Constitution, the General Medical Council and their publication on Good Medical Practice, and be

Sheffield Medical School

aware of current health news, controversial ethical dilemmas and politics surrounding the NHS. Also, applicants should answer appropriately why they have picked Sheffield, and demonstrable ability to overcome setbacks, work independently, take on responsibility, have good communication skills, are enthusiastic, with perseverance and self-insight.

Interview Season

December to March

Interview Outcome

March

Accommodation - Guarantee of Halls

Accommodation guaranteed for first year students

Student Perspective

Unique Selling Points

- Flexibility in course structure
- Easy to get involved in research
- Award winning student union

Things to Consider

- Travel far to clinical placements
- The surroundings can have steep inclines and hills
- Strict resit criteria

University of Southampton - School of Medicine

Contact Details

University of Southampton, University Road, Southampton, SO17 1BJ

E: ugapply.fm@southampton.ac.uk

T: 02380595000 / 02380594408

Courses Offered

A100

A101 (Graduate Entry)

A102 (Widening Access Programme)

Background

Medicine has been taught at the university for over 40 years. There are six campuses. As an undergraduate, most of your time in the first two years will be spent at Highfield Campus (where most of the academic courses are located) and Southampton General Hospital. Students on the graduate programme will spend most of their time at North Hampshire Hospital in Basingstoke and the Royal Hampshire County Hospital in Winchester.

Course Information

Southampton teaches by body systems: where students are taught all aspects for that system e.g. anatomy, physiology and pharmacology before moving on to the next system. The course is taught through lectures and some small group teaching.

Anatomy

Prosection is a compulsory part of the course. Dissection is not offered

Intercalation

Studying the A100 course enables students to be awarded the Bachelor of Medical Science (BMedSci) degree. This is a compulsory component and occurs in year 3. There is an option for intercalation between year 3 and 4 to take a Masters in Medical Science (25 places). Applicants are selected based on their performance during the programme. You are allowed to intercalate at other universities.

University of Southampton - School of Medicine

Elective

Minimum 4 weeks in an 8 week block at the end of 5th year

Entry requirements - A100

Entrance Exam

UKCAT:

2017 = 1900 (1700 international students).

No available data for previous years.

A Levels

AAA to include chemistry and biology. General studies and critical thinking are not accepted. A levels that have content overlap may not be taken in combination at A2 level such as human biology, sports studies or physical education.

International Baccalaureate

36 points with 18 in three subjects at Higher level (6 in chemistry and biology)

Scottish Highers

The university is currently reviewing the entry requirements for this qualification. Contact admissions.

Welsh Baccalaureate

The Welsh Baccalaureate Diploma will be accepted in lieu of one A level

GCSEs

Minimum of seven GCSES at grade B to include english language, maths and double award science

Mature non-graduate applicants (over the age of 21)

A levels: AAA to include chemistry and biology. If you have a nursing qualification, you must still have minimum two A levels at grade A in biology and chemistry. GCSEs: minimum grade C in english language, maths and double award science.

Graduates

Same requirements as graduates applying for the A101 programme

Access Courses Accepted

No specific access courses listed on the website (contact admissions for advice)

Entry Requirements - A101

Entrance Exam

UKCAT:

2015/16 = 2100

No data for previous years

Degree

Upper 2:1 in their first degree in any subject

A Levels

Minimum grade C in chemistry. If chemistry not taken at A2 then AS chemistry and biology/human biology at minimum grade C needs to have been taken.

GCSEs

Minimum grade C in english language, maths and double award science

Entry requirements - A102

Year zero involves three days at university per week which allows students to do some part-time work alongside their studies.

Entrance Exam

UKCAT: It tends not to be used to screen applicants for interview

Eligibility (satisfy three of the criteria and provide documentary evidence):

- Parents, guardian or applicant in receipt of a means-tested benefit
- Gets a 16-19 bursary or a similar grant
- Applicant looked after by a Local Authority
- Received free school meals at any point from Yr. 10-13
- First generation in their family to apply to higher education
- Lives in an area (postcode), which falls within the lowest 20% of the Index of Multiple Deprivation (will be confirmed by the University) or a member of a travelling family.

You cannot apply if you are an international student, graduate or have enrolled at some point on a higher education programme.

A Levels

BBC to include chemistry and biology. General studies

University of Southampton - School of Medicine

and critical thinking are not accepted. A levels that have content overlap may not be taken in combination at A2 level such as human biology, sports studies or physical education.

GCSEs

Minimum grade C in five GCSEs to include english language, maths and double award science

Progress to A100

Satisfactory completion of Year zero enables progression onto the A100 programme

Extra Application Information

- Resits for A levels: Resits for A levels or GCSEs are not accepted. In exceptional circumstances, applicants who are mature non-graduates (older than 21) or applying to the A102 programme may be looked at on a case-by-case basis. A levels should be taken at one sitting and within 2 years. A levels taken early are not considered.
- UCAS reapplication: Can reapply with no limit to number of applications.
- Deferred entry: Accepted but should be done at the time of UCAS submission. Requests later must be made in writing before confirmation in August and there is no guarantee that it will be accepted.
- Medical school transfers: Not offered
- Internal transfers: Not offered

Admissions Data

Number of applications - A100: 1414, A101: 1240, A102: 570
Number of interview places - A100: 600-700, A101: 190-200, A102: 120
Total number on course - A100: 202 (10-20), A101: 40, A102: 30

Applications
Non-academic Requirements

Students must show they have learnt from experiences of interacting with people; can be looking after an ill family member, voluntary work in a nursing home or homeless shelter, shadowing in a clinical setting or working with a special needs group.
For the A102 course, you need to be able to demonstrate a commitment to becoming a doctor, but you do not need to have work experience in a clinical setting.

Interview Selection

A100 and A101: ranked by UKCAT score first and then pre-screened against academic criteria. Invited to interview if academic criteria met and have appropriate UKCAT score.
A102: Applicants must take the UKCAT test but it is not used to decide who is invited to interview. You will be pre-screened against academic and eligibility criteria
All who meet the above criteria will be offered an interview. If there are too many applications, then each application will be reviewed regarding the non-academic criteria and interview places offered based on this.

Interview Information

Applicants will have to complete an interview (20 mins) with 2 interviewers (clinical and/or teaching staff) and a group task with 8 people (30 mins). Scores from interviews determine who gets an offer.

Interview Season

January to March

Interview Outcome

By the end of March

Accommodation - Guarantee of Halls

All applicants are guaranteed accommodation provided they meet the deadline. A102 applicants can apply for accommodation in year zero and year one.

Student Perspective
Unique Selling Points

- The majority of 3rd year is taken up with the research project for the BMedSci degree which is a great opportunity to gain research experience without taking up an extra year
- Southampton is only an hour and a half away from London by train
- Medical students at Southampton tend to help each other rather than compete with each other

Things to Consider

- Teaching on global health and social issues is limited and tends to be taught in a less engaging way
- Some academics will expect you to prepare for their class e.g anatomy, histology, it is really important that you do as otherwise you can get lost easily
- There is not a lot to do in Southampton as a city

University of St. Andrew's - School of Medicine

Contact Details

School of Medicine, University of St Andrews, North Haugh, St Andrews, KY16 9TF

E: medadmiss@st-andrews.ac.uk

T: 01334463599

Courses Offered

A100

A101 (Graduate Entry - New for 2018 Entry)

Gateway to Medicine (Foundation Year - direct application to university)

Background

Medicine has been taught at St Andrews since 1413. The facilities were updated in 2010 to give the UK's most modern medical school. Students study for three years and graduate from St. Andrews before continuing with their studies at one of the partner medical schools. Scot-GEM is the new graduate programme with the first cohort starting in 2018: it is a joint programme between St.Andrews and Dundee university and is in partnership with the University of the Highlands and Islands. Applications and decisions will be through St Andrews. The degree is ideal for those interested in a generalist career working in underserved areas, including opportunities to train in remote and rural areas.

Course Information

Teaching is heavily based with lectures with tutorials, case based discussions and labs 2-3 times a week. Clinical skills teaching is almost every week. Every year there are clinical attachments, usually for a couple of days a term.

Anatomy

Dissection sessions are compulsory and are scheduled most weeks in the 1st and 2nd years and a few times in the first half of the 3rd year. Students work in groups of 6-8 with tutors to guide the dissection session.

Intercalation

An honours-level research dissertation is completed at the end of 3rd year so students graduate with a BSc honours in medicine. This is a compulsory part of the course and there is no option to do this externally.

University of St. Andrew's - School of Medicine

Elective

Not offered as you transfer to another medical school for clinical years and will do elective then.

Entry requirements - A100
Entrance Exam
UKCAT: 2016 = 2400

A Levels

AAA to include chemistry and one other from biology, maths and physics. Only one of maths or further maths is counted for the 3 A levels. If biology, maths and English are not offered at A or AS level, each subject must have minimum grade B at GCSE. Dual award Science is not acceptable instead of GCSE biology. Human biology is equivalent to biology. General Studies, Critical Thinking, and Global Perspectives & Research are not acceptable.

International Baccalaureate

38 points. 666 at Higher level to include chemistry and one from biology, maths and physics. 666 at Standard level to include maths and/or biology if lacking at Higher level. A pass is required in english if it was not taken at Higher level. Standard level mathematics studies is not acceptable. The hours of science studied in the last two years of a school leaving qualification will be looked at.

Scottish Highers

AAAAB achieved in Highers in S5 to include grade A in chemistry and one from biology, maths and physics. Grade B in chemistry may be considered if they sit Advanced Higher chemistry in S6. Highers should be obtained at the same sitting; exceptions may be made if the school is unable to put applicants in for five Highers at one sitting. If biology, mathematics and english are not passed at Higher grade, they must have grade A or B in them at Intermediate 2 or at National 5. Human biology is equal to biology. If applicants have missing sciences in S5, they must take them in S6. BBB achieved in Highers/ Advanced Highers in S6. In the same year two science subjects must be sat- this can be in S5 or S6. A mix of Highers and Advanced Highers or just Advanced Highers are acceptable.

Welsh Baccalaureate

Currently under review for 2018 entry, please contact admissions

GCSEs

Minimum of 8 A grades or 6 A* grades in one sitting

Graduates

Minimum upper 2:1 achieved within the last five years in a science degree. A PhD will ameliorate for a degree that is older than 5 years (contact admissions for advice). Will need to obtain an academic transcript of their performance. Chemistry (Higher/ Advanced Higher/ A level) at grade A on first sitting to have achieved within the last 6 years. Applicants will be still be considered if they obtain chemistry at Higher/ Advanced Higher/ A level post degree. Applicants with an upper 2:1 or 1:1 degree in chemistry or a degree with a substantial chemistry element do not have chemistry at A level and equivalent. Grade B in biology, maths and english at GCSEs.

Access Courses Accepted

The only accepted access course is the HNC Applied Sciences Pathway to Medicine at Perth College.

Entry Requirements - Gateway to Medicine
Eligibility

Only applicants who have just completed S5 (Scottish A level equivalent). You should meet some of the following criteria listed below:

- Attended the Sutton Trust Summer School or engaged with the REACH project at St Andrews
- First generation applicant to higher education
- Live in an area of socio-economic disadvantage
- Be eligible for free school meals
- Be looked after/have been looked after by the Local Authority
- In receipt of an Education Maintenance Allowance (EMA)
- Attend a school, which has low figures of students who progress to higher education

Entrance Exam

UKCAT

Scottish Highers

AAAB at Scottish Higher S5 in one sitting to include chemistry and one other from physics, maths and physics. If biology, maths and english have not been passed at Higher, a grade A or B must have been achieved for each at Intermediate 2 or National 5.

University of St. Andrew's - School of Medicine

Application

You need to email the schools access office to show you are interested, who will confirm your eligibility to apply. Application by direct application form will occur immediately after Scottish Higher results are published. Interviews will take place and offers will be made so that applicants can start the programme in September of the same year.

Progress to A100

In order to progress to A100, applicants will need a minimum grade of 12.0 on their first sitting in each module and have achieved a suitable UKCAT score, either before entry to the 'Gateway' or in the summer after, and be successful in the MMI which occurs during the 'Gateway' year.

Entry Requirements - A101 (it is important to check the website as this is a new course and they have not finalised requirements yet)

Eligibility

Academic study within the last 3 years prior to entry

Entrance Exam

GAMSAT and the Situational Judgement Test (SJT) for Admission to Clinical Education (SJTACE). If you are already taking the UKCAT, the SJT subsection will be counted and you will not need to sit the SJTACE.

Degree

Upper 2:1 or 1:1 in arts or science honours degrees. Applicants will not be considered if they did not achieve the above level in their first degree even if they have gained a Masters or PhD.

A Levels/ Highers

Grade A/ B in chemistry at Higher/ A level

GCSEs/ Standards

Grade B in maths GCSE or maths Standard grade of Credit 1 or 2 or Intermediate 2/ National 5 grade A or B

Extra Application Information

- Resits for A levels: A levels need to be taken within the normal 2 years, applicants who take longer may be considered if there is evidence of extenuating circumstances. Retaking of AS modules are allowed as long as it is within the 2 years of study. Applicants who have had a change in career and so have taken new subjects may be considered if they have a strong previous academic performance and excellent predicted grades; three A levels sat within one sitting is still needed.
- UCAS reapplication: Applicants are allowed to apply to St Andrews twice through UCAS (this includes ScotGEM-A101).
- Deferred entry: The university does not usually consider deferring
- Medical school transfers: After finishing their third year at St.Andrews, students transfer to one of the six medical schools offered. Students complete their clinical training and graduate at one of the following universities; Aberdeen, Dundee, Edinburgh, Glasgow, Manchester or Barts. It is compulsory to transfer and there is no option to stay on at St. Andrews.
- Internal transfers: Not offered

Admissions Data

Number of applications - A100: 1000, A101: new for 2018
Number of interview places - A100: 400, A101: new for 2018
Total number on course - A100: 170, A101: new for 2018

Applications
Non-academic Requirements

The university is looking for a commitment to medicine shown by work experience/shadowing with ill or disabled people (preferably in a health-care setting).

Interview Selection

Applicants must have a strong academic record, a positive reference and medically related work experience to be considered. If the requirements above are met, applicants are ranked on their UKCAT score and the top ranking will be interviewed.

Interview Information

MMIs which will include 6 or more stations. Communication and interpersonal skills will be looked at on each station. At least one station will involve an actor and role-play. The student's ability to discuss ethical issues will also be assessed. Scoring for offers will be based on the interview (the situational judgement test will be incorporated into this score) and the UKCAT score.

University of St. Andrew's - School of Medicine

A101 interview will be in the form of MMIs but will be conducted at the University of Dundee.

Interview Season
December to March

Interview Outcome
You may hear an outcome throughout the interview season but the majority of decisions are not made until mid-March.

Accommodation - Guarantee of Halls
Undergraduate students are guaranteed accommodation in their first year providing they apply by the deadline. Each halls has a mixture of first year students and students from other years.

Student Perspective
Unique Selling Points
- The structure of the course allows students to experience two universities
- All teaching happens in a dedicated, modern building with an amazing clinical suite which is used from the 1st year
- The smallness of the city means that there are always people around that you know and so it feels very friendly

Things to Consider
- It is quite a difficult location to get to
- It can be expensive to live especially for rent
- You have to re-integrate yourself at a new medical school after three years

St George's University of London

Contact Details
St George's University of London, Cranmer Terrace, London, SW17 ORE
E: admissions@sgul.ac.uk
T: 02086729944 / 02087252333

Courses Offered
A100
A101 (Graduate Entry)

Background
St George's has a history of teaching medicine for more than 250 years. St George's Hospital was opened in 1733 with formal registration of apprentice doctors in 1751.In 2000 it was the first University to launch the graduate entry programme (MBBS 4 year course) to graduates who had studied any degree. St George's shares its campus with one of the largest teaching hospitals in the UK

Course Information
Teaching is based around case based learning in the pre-clinical years where a tutorial is planned for the beginning and end of the week to discuss clinical cases. Problem based learning becomes more prominent in the third year onwards. Lectures and clinical and communication skills sessions also form part of the curriculum.

Anatomy
Anatomy is taught using whole body prosection and is led by demonstrators

Intercalation
Intercalation is offered between 3rd and 4th year and students can intercalate externally

Elective
6 weeks at the end of 5th year

Entry Requirements - A100
Entrance Exam
UKCAT: both the section scores (500 or above) and overall cut-offs must be met.
2016 = 2600, 2015 = 2550, 2014 = 2590

St George's University of London

A Levels

AAA to include chemistry and biology/human biology. General studies and key Skills are not accepted. Adjusted criteria - If your predicted/ actual grades are AAB-ABB then you will be considered in regards to the average A level point score per student at the school/college you attended (check the eligible schools/colleges list on the website).

International Baccalaureate

36 points. Higher level:18 points with a 6 in at least biology and chemistry.
Standard level: minimum score of 5 in maths and english. if the applicant has not achieved a minimum grade B in GCSE.

Scottish Highers

AAA in Highers to include chemistry and/or biology
AA in Advanced Highers to include chemistry and/ or biology
English language at minimum Standard grade 2

Welsh Baccalaureate

This is done on an individual case by case basis so check with the admissions department.

GCSEs

416 points from top eight GCSE subjects (equates to an average grade A)
A*=58, A=52, B=46, C=40, D=34, E=28
English language at minimum grade B
Maths and dual award science/ triple science

Graduates

Not allowed to apply for A100

Access Courses Accepted

Access to Medicine Diploma accepted in conjunction with minimum grade B in GCSE english and maths

Entry Requirements - A101
Entrance Exam

GAMSAT: Both section (minimum of 50) and overall cut-off scores need to be met - 2015 = 62

Degree

2:1 in any discipline or a postgraduate degree with a minimum pass (MSc, MPhil, PhD). The postgraduate degree must be completed and awarded including viva and re-writes by 1St August in the year of entry. If you are a current healthcare professional, you must provide details of your registration.

Extra Application Information

- Resits for A levels: With the exception of GCSEs all qualifications must have been finished within the last five years (including the year of application). Grades need to be from one sitting. A levels need to be completed within 2 years.
- UCAS reapplication: Applicants are limited to two applications if you reach interview stage. There are no caps on applications if applicants do not get through to interview stage.
- Deferred entry: The university does not recommend this, as applicants will still be made to re-interview with the cohort they will be joining and there is no guarantee they will be made another offer.
- Medical school transfers: Not offered
- Internal transfers: Not offered

Admissions Data

Number of applications - A100: 1100, A101: 1400
Number of interview places - A100: 700, A101: 300-400
Total number on course - A100: 185, A101: 60
The university are unable to confirm how many spaces are allocated for international students.

Applications
Non-academic Requirements

You are expected to have gained voluntary/work experience in a healthcare related field and demonstrate an awareness of medicine. You must provide references for each separate piece of formal work experience you want to bring to interview that has been within the last 2 years (should include dates, hours worked and duties, it does not need to include a character reference). Applicants are expected to have experience in healthcare and non-healthcare settings and be able to explain what you contributed and learnt as well as knowing your own abilities and limitations. Experiences that show you have made a regular commitment are preferred.

Interview Selection

UKCAT results are used to select applicants for interview

St George's University of London

Interview Information

MMIs with up to eight stations each lasting 5 minutes, lasting for a total of 40 minutes. Examples of tasks are included on the website under 'Apply'. Offers are made based on performance at interview. If there were a tie between two students, the UKCAT/GAMSAT overall score would be used.

Interview Season

December to April

Interview Outcome

On a rolling basis, will normally hear a few weeks after your interview

Accommodation - Guarantee of Halls

Undergraduate and international applicants are prioritised for accommodation. If students are unable to secure a room, there are halls available at the intercollegiate halls of residence (run by the University of London) and private accommodation.

Student Perspective
Unique Selling Points

- The university focuses on interprofessional learning, which means medical students, learn from and with students from other courses. This prepares students for working in a multi-disciplinary team in a hospital.
- Focus on teaching communication skills so students can communicate effectively with patients from different backgrounds.
- Emphasis on small group teaching, which includes case based learning, PBLs and dissection.

Things to Consider

- There is no guarantee of accommodation at the university, although there is plenty of accommodation to be found in London.
- Deferred entry is not really an option.
- You do not get to do dissection yourself, as anatomy is taught using cadavers that have already been dissected.

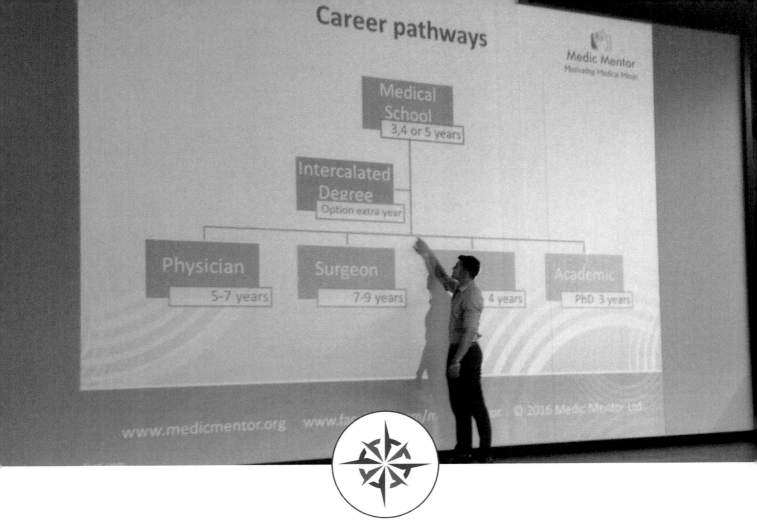

Swansea University Medical School

Contact Details

Swansea University Medical School, Grove Building, Swansea University, Singleton Park, Swansea, SA2 8PP

E: mededucation.unit@swansea.ac.uk

T: 01792513400 / 01792 51342

Courses Offered

A101 (Graduate Entry)

Background

The graduate medical school was developed from the clinical school in 2004. in 2009 the graduate programme started to be taught entirely at Swansea University. Within the graduate curriculum there is a scheme called Rural and Remote Health in Medical Education where selected students spend more time in rural health environments including their elective (rural and remote area abroad).

Course Information

Swansea follows a spiral curriculum: the body systems are taught in learning weeks, which are then revisited later on. Each learning week is structured so that all the teaching sessions link back to the case of the week. The course is taught through lectures, tutorials and clinical skills sessions. A practising doctor in that speciality often carries out the teaching. There is the option to choose a Welsh-speaking personal tutor if available as well as submitting some assignments in Welsh.

Anatomy

Anatomy is taught using mainly prosections. There is the opportunity to arrange to see a dissection or a post mortem. Students have access to models, computer apps and 3D technology to help aid learning.

Intercalation

Not offered, as it is a graduate only course

Elective

6 weeks at the end of 3rd year

Entry Requirements - A101

Entrance Exam

GAMSAT: cut-off score has been 57 for the past few years.

Swansea University Medical School

Overall score of at least 50, with at least 50 in paper 3 (reasoning in biological and physical sciences)

Degree

Upper 2:1 in any subject or Merit (equivalent to 2:1) in an integrated undergraduate Masters degree or Lower 2:2 with a postgraduate Masters or PhD

Qualifications must be completed and verified by 31st July in the year of starting the course. Your predicted grade should be included in the academic reference. Undergraduate students studying medical biochemistry, medical genetics and applied medical sciences at Swansea are guaranteed an interview for the programme provided they meet the minimum entry criteria.

GCSEs

Mathematics and english/ Welsh at minimum grade C

Extra Application Information

- Resits for A levels: Not applicable
- UCAS reapplication: Can reapply with no limit to number of applications
- Deferred entry: Not accepted
- Medical school transfers: Not offered
- Internal transfers: Not offered

Admissions Data

Number of applications - A101: 1000
Number of interview places - A101: 300
Total number on course - A101: 75 (5)

Applications

Non-academic Requirements

Any type of work experience will be valued on your application and will be focused on during the interview.

Interview Selection

Applicants who meet the academic requirements are then invited to interview based on their GAMSAT scores.

Interview Information

Applicants can choose to have their interview in Welsh if preferred. Interview consists of a written situational judgement test (30 mins) and two interviews (each 20 mins). There will be two interviewers on each panel and can be: clinicians, academics, medical students or members of the public. Your personal statement will also be discussed. Those applicants who score the highest will be offered places.

Interview Season

March

Interview Outcome

The University will let you know as soon as possible. There is a waiting list and in some cases, students will be given an offer up to August 31st.

Accommodation - Guarantee of Halls

Guaranteed accommodation for students provided they hold and accept a firm offer and make an application by the deadline.

Student Perspective
Unique Selling Points

- From the 1st year you get early exposure in a hospital in a chosen specialty (up to five weeks)
- The medical school year size is small: this means you get to know your fellow students well
- Beautiful area to study as there are beaches (surfing if you are into it), parks and countryside

Things to Consider

- The choice of medical school societies is smaller due to the cohort size
- Elective is in the 3rd year rather than 4th/final year when you have more experience
- A car would be helpful for the more remote placements especially if you keen to apply for the Rural and Remote Health in Medical Education scheme

University of Central Lancashire –
The School of Medicine

Contact Details

The School of Medicine, University of Central Lancashire, Preston, Lancashire, PR1 2HE

E: mbbsscholarships@uclan.ac.uk (specific to scholarships)

T: 01772893699 / 01772892400

Courses Offered

A100

Background

University of Central Lancashire (UCLan) is a private university set up to offer a UK medical qualification for international (non-EU) students. The university was set up in 1828, but the medical school is extremely new and was opened in 2014. There are 2 scholarships available for UK students and the scholarship covers the tuition fees for the entire course, clinical placements costs and a bursary that is equal to what would be offered from Student Finance England for living costs.

Course Information

The course is taught through small group tutorials, labs, workshops and seminars. It is taught by going through the body systems. In 3rd and 4th year, you will spend one day per week at the university for teaching and the rest of the time will be on placements. 5th year will be spent almost entirely on clinical placements.

Anatomy

Virtual dissection tables are used to teach anatomy in the Human Anatomy Resource and Learning Centres. The dissection tables show real images of cadavers or patient scans and you use your hand to slice through the 3D image rather than a scalpel.

Intercalation

Option to intercalate after 4th year in a Masters

Elective

Optional - offered between 4th and 5th year

University of Central Lancashire - The School of Medicine

Entry requirements - A100 (UK Scholarship Programme)

Entrance Exam

No entrance exam is required

Eligibility

Students need to live and go to a school in one of the following areas: Accrington, Allerdale or the wider Cumbria region, Blackburn with Darwen, Burnley, Copeland, Pendle, the Ribble Valley and Rossendale.

The university welcomes applications from students estranged from their parents, care leavers, young adult carers, low income families and students who are the first to go on to higher education in their family.

A Levels

AAB to include two sciences of which one must be chemistry and a third academic subject.

International Baccalaureate

36 points to include chemistry, another science and one other subject at Higher level. Minimum 5 points in each of the 3 subjects at Standard level.

GCSEs

Must be able to provide evidence of continued academic study to include science and maths up to the age of 15/16

Graduates

2:1 in any science subject OR 2:1 in a healthcare degree with at least a year of professional work experience

Extra Application Information

- Resits for A levels: Grades are expected to be achieved on the first sitting.
- UCAS reapplication: The scholarships are new for 2017 entry, so contact admissions to confirm.
- Deferred entry: The scholarships are new for 2017 entry, so contact admissions to confirm.
- Medical School Transfers: Not offered
- Internal Transfers: Not offered

Admissions Data

Number of applications - A100: the scholarships are new for 2017 entry so data not available

Number of interview places - A100: the scholarships are new for 2017 entry so data not available

Total number on course - A100: 65 (2 spaces for UK students)

Applications

Non-academic Requirements

The university expects you to try and get some work experience in a clinical setting such as hospital, GP or hospice. If you have not managed to obtain any, they appreciate voluntary work. You must have letters confirming work experience or volunteering that you have completed along with this you are expected to complete a transferable skills statement and both of these have to be sent by email to the university.

Scholarship Workshop

UK Students who are eligible to apply for the scholarships can email mbbsscholarships@uclan.ac.uk to ask for a place on the workshop so they can get advice on the application and what happens at the interview.

Interview Selection

You should apply through UCAS. Students should include information on how they meet the scholarship criteria in their personal statement. Furthermore, students will need to submit a 300-word statement indicating their suitability based on the widening participation criteria.

Academic criteria and eligibility criteria will be checked and if the applicant meets these their application will be assessed. The personal statement, transferable skills statement and reference will be used together to determine whom to interview.

Interview Information

MMIs, which consists of 8 stations. Applicants who pass 6 out of 8 stations are ranked and offers will be made to the applicants with the highest-ranking scores.

Interview Season

March

Interview Outcome

After March

University of Central Lancashire - The School of Medicine

Accommodation - Guarantee of Halls

You can apply for accommodation on the Burnley Campus and will be notified by the admissions team to apply if you confirm UCLan as your firm choice.

Student Perspective

Unique Selling Points

- The university has state of the art facilities with clinical skills laboratories with human simulators that are setup to replicate ward and GP environments
- Small cohort which means you will get to know all the students in your year
- The scholarships for UK students covers tuition fees and a bursary that is equivalent to Student Finance England, meaning less worries financially

Things to Consider

- The university is going through review by the GMC year by year until the first cohort graduates in order for them to let UCLan award a GMC recognised medical qualification. If this isn't the case, arrangements have been put in place for students to graduate from the University of Liverpool with the GMC recognised medical qualification.
- There are only two spaces for UK students and all other students will be international students
- It is an extremely new course and the first cohort has not graduated yet

University College London (UCL) Medical School

Contact Details

University College London, Gower Street, London, WC1E 6BT

E: medicaladmissions@ucl.ac.uk

T: 020 7679 2000 / 020 3108 8228 / 020 3108 8235

Courses Offered

A100

Background

UCL formed from the joining of several medical schools; Middlesex Hospital and University College Hospital medical schools merged in 1987 and then joined the Royal Free Hospital Medical School in 1998. The medical school is linked with Great Ormond Street Hospital, the National Hospital for Neurology and Neurosurgery, the Royal Hospital for Neurology and Neurosurgery and Moorfields Eye Hospital. There are three main campuses; Royal Free, Bloomsbury and Whittington.

Course Information

The course is heavily lecture-based for the first two years with some small group weekly teaching in groups of around 12-14. In clinical years there are a week's worth of lectures per term with the majority of time spent on placements.

Anatomy

Dissection of cadavers is a compulsory part of the timetable

Intercalation

Intercalation is a compulsory part of the undergraduate degree for school leavers. There is no option to intercalate externally. Graduate entrants with UK degrees do not undertake an intercalated year and so the course length is 5 years.

Elective

7 weeks in 5th year

Entry requirements - A100
Entrance Exam

BMAT:

Mean scores for 2017 were: section 1 = 4.7, section 2 = 4.8 and section 3 = 3.1A

University College London (UCL) Medical School

Mean scores for 2016 were: section 1 = 5.3, section 2 = 5.3 and section 3 = 3.3A
Mean Scores for section 1 and 2 are normally between 4.5-5.5 and section 3 is normally around 3.

A Levels

A*AA to include biology and chemistry, an A* is required in one of these two sciences. Critical thinking and general studies are not accepted.

International Baccalaureate

Minimum is 39 points, with minimum of 19 points in 3 Higher level subjects to include biology and chemistry (one at grade 7 and one at grade 6). No score should be below 5.

Scottish Highers

A1AA at Advanced Highers to include chemistry and biology or A1A at Advanced Higher and AAA at Higher

Welsh Baccalaureate

Successful completion of the Advanced Skills Challenge Certificate with A*AA at A level to include chemistry and biology

GCSEs

Grade B or above in english language and maths. For UK based students, a foreign language grade C or above is needed (this does not include Ancient Greek, Biblical Hebrew or Latin). There is the chance to meet this requirement following enrolment.

Graduates

Upper 2.1 in science or non-science degree. ABB in A levels or 6, 5, 5 in IB to include chemistry and biology taken before their degree. If the degree contains chemistry and biology, this may be accepted instead of A levels, but the modules studied must be submitted for consideration in plenty of advance of the 15th October. A* or A in A levels taken after degree.

Access Courses Accepted

The only one accepted is the Access to HE Diploma (Medicine) from the College of West Anglia.

Extra Application Information

- Resits for A levels: A2 level re-sits are not accepted outside the standard 2 years.

- UCAS reapplication: Applications will not be considered if the applicant was unsuccessful after an interview in a previous application cycle.
- Deferred entry: Applicants are welcome to apply for deferred entry on their application. Applicants need to be prepared to talk about their plans on their gap year during interview.
- Medical school transfers: Not offered
- Internal transfers: Not offered

Admissions Data

Number of applications - A100: 2500
Number of interview places - A100: 700
Total number on course - A100: 322 (24)
There are no set allocated places for graduates applying to do the 5 year course.

Applications
Non-academic Requirements

The university advises applicants to read the work experience guide on the medical schools council website. The university reviews a sample of students and asks to see evidence of work experience. Therefore, applicants should keep letters and references from work experience placements and to create a table or list summarising the work experience undertaken.

Interview Selection

All applications are read (personal statement and references) and all information including BMAT scores will be taken into consideration before a decision is made. They do not use a cut-off score for BMAT.

Interview Information

Both graduates and school leavers are assessed together. It is a panel interview with 2-3 interviewers (includes clinical medical staff, a senior medical student or lay interviewer such as GP or Head of Sixth Form). The interview usually lasts 15-20 minutes. Applicants need to be prepared to discuss their BMAT essay as interviewers will have a copy.

Interview Season

December to mid-March (January normally for graduate students and gap year students and school leavers normally February to March)

University College London (UCL) Medical School

Interview Outcome

Should hear outcome of the interview within 14 days

Accommodation - Guarantee of Halls

Accommodation is guaranteed for first year students if applicants firmly accept an offer for UCL and have not previously lived or studied within the M25 as a student at another university/college.

Student Perspective

Unique Selling Points

- There are opportunities to see rare diseases at big tertiary centres in London
- The university teaches global and public health extremely well
- UCL are quite language focused and there are multiple opportunities to learn languages with bursaries available

Things to Consider

- The group teaching sessions are quite large
- There is minimal dermatology teaching and no exposure to cardiothoracic or plastic surgery
- There is no chance to resit in fourth and fifth year, so if you don't pass the year, you have to retake the year

Warwick Medical School

Contact Details
Warwick Medical School, University of Warwick, Coventry, CV4 7AL
E: pgteam1@warwick.ac.uk
T: 02476574880 / 02476524585

Courses Offered
A101 (Graduate Entry)

Background
Warwick Medical School started in 2000 as a joint programme between Leicester and Warwick Universities. In 2007, Warwick Medical School stopped the joint programme with Leicester as it was awarded independent degree-awarding status. Warwick medical school runs the largest graduate medicine programme in the UK.

Course Information
The course is taught through CBL (case based learning) where small groups of 10 students work through the case together as well as lectures, workshops and bedside teaching in hospital.

Anatomy
Anatomy is taught using plastinates in first year, which happens weekly at the hospital. Junior doctors help support these sessions. Dissection is not offered although very occasionally you may look at prosections.

Intercalation
Not offered as it is a graduate only course

Elective
6 weeks in 4th year (final year) after finals

Entry Requirements - A101
Entrance Exam
UKCAT: Verbal Reasoning is used for selection. Those applicants who score lower than the average mean score for that year will be rejected. Applicants who get through based on verbal reasoning score then have their total UKCAT scored and ranked.

Total score: 2016 = 2770, 2015 = 2800, 2014 = 2940

Warwick Medical School

Degree

Upper 2:1 in any undergraduate subject or lower 2:1 with a Masters or a doctoral qualification or intercalated Masters at minimum pass grade

Extra Application Information

- Resits for A levels: Not applicable
- UCAS reapplication: Can reapply with no limit to number of applications
- Deferred entry: Not accepted
- Medical school transfers: Not offered
- Internal transfers: Not offered

Admissions Data

Number of applications - A101: 1500

Number of interview places - A101: 380

Total number on course - A101: 177 (13)

Applications

Non-academic Requirements

Minimum work experience expected is 70 hours (approximately two weeks full time) over the previous three years. There must be a minimum of two work placements with not one placement counting for more than 50 hours. Experience that is valued includes volunteering at a nursing home, care home, hospice, hospital employment or a professional healthcare job. You need to show evidence of providing personal hands-on care to individuals who are not your friends or family. You also need to show you have spent work experience shadowing doctors and other healthcare professionals and have experience of a healthcare environment. Candidates are expected to provide references (including details of the role, how you met the criteria-see work experience section, and the number of hours you were there for) from your work experience to bring to the interview.

Interview Selection

Verbal reasoning is used for selection. Applicants who get through based on verbal reasoning score then have their total UKCAT scored and ranked. Applicants are awarded points based on their highest academic qualifications. Points will only be given for PhD and Masters, which have been awarded by the UCAS deadline. The personal statement is not used as part of the selection process.

Interview Information

MMIs, which is made up of six stations. Interviewers include doctors, academics and members of the public. Scores will be totalled and the applicants scoring the highest will be given an offer.

Interview Season

January

Interview Outcome

Normally within one month after the interview

Accommodation - Guarantee of Halls

You are not guaranteed accommodation. The earlier you apply the more likely you will get accommodation. As a graduate, you will normally be placed in Tocil with other postgraduates.

Student Perspective

Unique Selling Points

- It is the biggest graduate only medicine course in the UK, and this means that everyone is determined and focused on their career as they have already experienced university before
- There are 3 sets of exams over 4 years, these are in 1st year, 2nd year and 4th years
- It is a relatively small medical school and so this breeds a supportive environment where you feel supported by clinicians, peers and you get teaching from the year above

Things to consider

- It is worthwhile thinking about bringing a car as placements can be in the countryside and can be difficult to get to
- The Warwick University campus is not actually in Warwick, but situated near Coventry
- There is no guarantee of accommodation on campus